C901154493

KU-443-470

HIGHER
GCSE MATHEMATICS
FOR CCEA

Anne Connolly
Linda Liggett
Robin Liggett

PRACTICE BOOK

HODDER
EDUCATION
AN HACHETTE UK COMPANY

Although every effort has been made to ensure that website addresses are correct at time of going to press, Hodder Education cannot be held responsible for the content of any website mentioned. It is sometimes possible to find a relocated web page by typing in the address of the home page for a website in the URL window of your browser.

Orders: please contact Bookpoint Ltd, 130 Milton Park, Abingdon, Oxon OX14 4SB. Telephone: (44) 01235 827720. Fax: (44) 01235 400454. Lines are open 9.00–17.00, Monday to Saturday, with a 24-hour message answering service. Visit our website at www.hoddereducation.co.uk

© Anne Connolly, Robin Liggett, Linda Liggett, Howard Baxter, Mike Handbury, John Jeskins, Jean Matthews, Mark Patmore, Brian Seager, Colin White, Eddie Wilde 2014

First published in 2014 by
Hodder Education
An Hachette UK Company,
338 Euston Road
London NW1 3BH

Impression number	5	4	3	2	1
Year		2017	2016	2015	2014

All rights reserved. Apart from any use permitted under UK copyright law, no part of this publication may be reproduced or transmitted in any form or by any means, electronic or mechanical, including photocopying and recording, or held within any information storage and retrieval system, without permission in writing from the publisher or under licence from the Copyright Licensing Agency Limited. Further details of such licences (for reprographic reproduction) may be obtained from the Copyright Licensing Agency Limited, Saffron House, 6–10 Kirby Street, London EC1N 8TS.

Cover photo © Keren Su/Corbis

Typeset in 11 on 12 Bembo Regular by Integra Software Services Pvt. Ltd., Pondicherry, India

Printed in Great Britain by CPI Group (UK) Ltd, Croydon, CR0 4YY

A catalogue record for this title is available from the British Library

ISBN 978 1 4718 0080 1

Contents

Introduction

This book contains questions designed for the Higher tier of GCSE Mathematics. It covers the CCEA specification for the modules T3, T4 and T6.

Each chapter matches one in the CCEA Higher GCSE textbook. This book can be used in conjunction with the textbook or separately on its own. Some of the larger chapters have more than one exercise.

On the contents page, the chapters indicated by an arrowhead are T6. In some chapters there is an overlap with T3, T4 and T6 topics. For example, chapters 6 and 15.

There are lots of questions in each chapter to provide practice, build confidence and produce satisfaction in being able to do Mathematics. There are problem-solving questions that give opportunities for Mathematics to be used in every day contexts. The questions usually start out by being quite straightforward. Towards the end of each chapter there are some more challenging questions.

Many of the questions can be completed without a calculator. When a calculator is used, we encourage every step of the working out to be shown in your solution.

At the start of every chapter there is a brief summary of what you will be covering as you work through the questions.

The book has been designed to help prepare students for the Mathematics GCSE exam. Doing every question in this book will certainly do that!

CHAPTER 1

Language of number

This chapter is about

- being able to find the square, cube, square root, cube root of numbers
- writing any number as a product of primes
- finding the HCF and LCM of pairs of numbers.

1 For the numbers 14, 18, 24, 25 and 60, write down which has a factor of
  a 3
  b 5
  c 12
  d both 6 and 8
  e both 6 and 15.

2 Look at these numbers: 4, 12, 17, 21, 35.
  a Which have a factor of 2?
  b Which have a factor of 5?
  c Which have a factor of 3?
  d Which of these numbers are prime numbers?

3 Look at these numbers: 1, 2, 5, 15, 17, 18. Write down those that are
  a multiples of 2
  b factors of 50
  c multiples of 3
  d prime numbers.

4 Write down the value of
  a 6^2 **b** 1^2 **c** 10^2 **d** 5^2 **e** 11^2
  f 4^3 **g** 1^3 **h** 10^3 **i** 0.7^2 **j** 8^1

5 Write down the value of
  a $\sqrt{49}$ **b** $\sqrt{9}$ **c** $\sqrt{81}$ **d** $\sqrt{100}$ **e** $\sqrt[3]{216}$
  f $\sqrt{1}$ **g** $\sqrt[3]{1000}$ **h** $\sqrt[3]{1}$ **i** $\sqrt[3]{8}$ **j** $\sqrt{0.36}$

6 Write down the value of
  a $8^2 - 6^2$ **b** $7^2 + 4^2$ **c** $5^3 - 2^3$ **d** $5^2 + 6^3 + 7^2$

7 Write these using index form.
  a $4 \times 4 \times 4$ **b** $7 \times 7 \times 7 \times 7$
  c $3 \times 3 \times 3 \times 3 \times 3 \times 3 \times 3 \times 3 \times 3$ **d** $9 \times 9 \times 9 \times 9 \times 9 \times 9$
  e $2 \times 2 \times 2 \times 2 \times 2 \times 2 \times 2$ **f** $4 \times 4 \times 5 \times 5 \times 5$
  g $8 \times 8 \times 3 \times 3 \times 8 \times 8$ **h** $2 \times 6 \times 6 \times 2 \times 2 \times 6 \times 6$

8 Find the value of each of these.
  a 2^4 **b** 1^6 **c** 4^5 **d** 7^4 **e** 2^8

9 Find the product of the first three prime numbers.

10 Find the sum of the 3 largest prime numbers which are less than 100.

11 Which factors of 60 are also multiples of 4?

12 Between which two consecutive whole numbers does the square root of 240 lie?

13 Express each of these numbers as a product of its prime factors. Give your answers using index notation where appropriate.

a 14	**b** 16	**c** 28	**d** 35
e 42	**f** 49	**g** 108	**h** 156
i 225	**j** 424	**k** 864	**l** 6930

14 a Given that $5292 = 2^a \times 3^b \times 7^c$ find a, b, c.
   b Given that $49005 = 3^x \times 5^y \times 11^z$ find x, y, z.
   c Given that $274400 = 2^m \times 5^n \times 7^p$ find m, n, p
   d Given that $214375 = 5^d \times 7^e$ find d, e

15 Find the HCF of

a 14 and 35	**b** 16 and 42
c 49 and 108	**d** 156 and 225
e 240 and 108	**f** 330 and 385
g 1240 and 1540	**h** 468 and 1300

16 Find the LCM of

a 16 and 42	**b** 28 and 35
c 108 and 156	**d** 225 and 424
e 450 and 210	**f** 810 and 735
g 1100 and 450	**h** 374 and 214

17 Work out the prime factorisation of these numbers and use it to write down the HCF and LCM of each pair.

a 84 and 154	**b** 75 and 135
c 150 and 95	**d** 645 and 225

18 Find the HCF and the LCM of each pair of numbers.
   a 17 and 40
   b 52 and 221
   c 77 and 98

19 Use prime factorisation to find the cube root of   **a** 21 952   **b** 85 184.

20 What does 5775 need to be multiplied by to make a square number?

21 Bus A passes a school every 80 minutes. Bus B passes the same school every 48 minutes. If they pass together at 9a.m., when do they next pass together?

CHAPTER 2

Whole numbers

This chapter is about

- adding and subtracting whole numbers
- multiplying and dividing by powers, and multiples of the powers of ten
- multiplying and dividing any whole numbers
- solving problems involving addition, subtraction, multiplication and division, and understanding the significance of the remainder in the context of division
- understanding inverse operations and using them as a checking procedure.

Do not use a calculator for any of these questions.

1 Calculate these.
  a 538 + 179   **b** 347 + 482   **c** 341 + 5631   **d** 272 + 61929
  e 321 + 4560   **f** 748 + 15709   **g** 2368 + 492518   **h** 8236 + 79 + 503

2 Calculate these.
  a 579 − 432   **b** 685 − 59   **c** 967 − 198   **d** 1468 − 157
  e 1785 − 532   **f** 2064 − 262   **g** 56023 − 1857   **h** 20307 − 8929

3 It is 403 miles from San Francisco to Los Angeles and then 127 miles from Los Angeles to San Diego. How far is it from San Francisco to San Diego?

4 Carmel has all of these numbers written on a piece of paper.

　　543　　123　　432　　234　　321　　345

She claims that she can make exactly 1000 by adding just three of the numbers together. Is this possible?

5 It is 1011 kilometres from Brisbane to Sydney and 957 kilometres from Sydney to Melbourne. How many more kilometres is it from Brisbane to Sydney than from Sydney to Melbourne?

6 Given that 5628 + 3179 = 8807, write down the answer only to
  a 8807 − 5628   **b** 8807 − 2179   **c** 8810 − 5628   **d** 6628 + 3179

7 Calculate these.
  a 36 × 100   **b** 2400 ÷ 10   **c** 520 × 10   **d** 12400 ÷ 100   **e** 9 × 1000

8 Calculate these.
  a 36 × 500   **b** 18 × 2000   **c** 36000 ÷ 90   **d** 8000 ÷ 400   **e** 126 × 20

9 Calculate these.
  a 47 × 82   **b** 54 × 79   **c** 516 × 65   **d** 3926 × 48   **e** 4053 × 917

10 Jill has 15 shelves of books in her study. Each shelf holds 24 books. How many books are there in her study?

11 Work out these.
  a 876 ÷ 17   **b** 864 ÷ 32   **c** 840 ÷ 24   **d** 8775 ÷ 27   **e** 27638 ÷ 40

12 423 people have booked to go on a special train excursion. Each carriage holds 56 people. How many carriages are needed?

13 In a cinema there are 828 seats. Each row has 36 seats. How many rows are there?

14 Peter opened a 500 g bag of dried pasta. He cooked for four people, using 75 g of pasta per person. How much pasta is left in the bag?

15 One week, Jean used her car for long journeys of 220 miles and 176 miles. At the beginning of the week her milometer showed 17 659. At the end of the week it showed 18 137.
For how many miles did she use her car for short journeys that week?

16 At the bakery, Joe bought four jam doughnuts costing 35p each and two Cornish pasties. He gave the assistant £5 and got £1.70 change.
How much did each Cornish pasty cost?

17 Given that $83 \times 260 = 21\,580$, write down the answer only to
    a $21\,580 \div 260$ **b** $21\,580 \div 830$

18 Given that $169\,600 \div 320 = 530$, write down the answer only to
    a 530×320 **b** $5\,300 \times 32$

19 Given that $2\,165 + 389 = 2\,554$, write down the answer only to
    a $2\,554 - 389$ **b** $3\,165 + 389$

20 Given that $150 \times 90 = 13\,500$, write down the answer only to
    a $1\,350 \div 9$ **b** 15×9

21 Given that $6158 - 1749 = 4409$, write down the answer only to
    a $4409 + 1749 + 3000$ **b** $(6158 - 4409) \times 100$

22 Given that $(87 + 53)^2 = 19600$, write down the answer only to
    a $\sqrt{19600}$ **b** $(87 + 53)^2 - 100^2$

CHAPTER 3

Decimals

This chapter is about

- understanding place value in decimals
- ordering decimals
- adding, subtracting, multiplying and dividing decimals, including multiplication and division by powers of ten, and multiples of powers of ten
- understanding the increasing and decreasing effect when multiplying and dividing by decimals
- solving problems involving decimals in context.

Do not use a calculator.

1 Calculate these.

    a 21.43 + 36.31   **b** 76.02 + 11.69
    c 34.986 + 42.37   **d** 37.845 − 15.49
    e 59.26 − 38.164   **f** 87.452 − 24.2736

2 Calculate these.

    a 0.6 × 8   **b** 1.8 × 4
    c 18.7 × 6   **d** 13.4 × 4
    e 3.6 × 1.4   **f** 5.8 × 2.6
    g 8.1 × 4.32   **h** 6.51 × 3.23
    i 74 × 1.7   **j** 0.64 × 3.8

3 Calculate these.

    a 7.2 ÷ 3   **b** 8.5 ÷ 5
    c 37.5 ÷ 3   **d** 54 ÷ 4
    e 12 ÷ 0.4   **f** 35 ÷ 0.7
    g 18.2 ÷ 0.7   **h** 31.2 ÷ 0.6
    i 3.614 ÷ 2.6   **j** 9.5846 ÷ 0.17

4 A wall is to be 25 m long. So far, the bricklayer has built 18.75 m. How much more has to be built?

5 An antique dealer bought two pictures, one for £35.50 and the other for 85p. He sold the two together for £90. How much money did he make?

6 Two pieces measuring 90 cm each are cut from a length of wood 2.4 m long. What length is left?

7 A paving slab is 59.5 cm long. What is the length of a path made by laying nine of these slabs in a line?

8 A carriage in a train is 29.8 m long. What is the total length of four carriages?

9 A stack of eight textbooks is 18.8 cm high. What is the height of a single textbook?

10 A packet of six large dice weighs 83.4 g. What is the weight of one die?

11 Given that 47 × 53 = 2491, write down the answers to these.

    a 4.7 × 5.3
    b 4.7 × 5300
    c 4.7 × 0.053
    d 0.47 × 5.3

12 Find the cost of six DVDs at £13.34 each.

13 Melissa buys three of these bags of carrots.

WEIGHT	PRICE
0.450 kg	99p

    a What is the total weight?
    b What is the total cost?

14 How many glasses holding 0.3 litre can be filled from a jug containing 1.7 litres?

15 John cycles to and from school each day. He lives 2.4 miles from the school. One weekend he cycled 17.6 miles. How many miles did he cycle altogether that week?

16 At the greengrocers, Harry bought four oranges costing 30p each, some bananas costing £1.08 and three grapefruit. He paid with a £5 note and was given £1.37 in change. How much did each grapefruit cost?

CHAPTER 4

Negative numbers

This chapter is about

- understanding and being able to use negative numbers in context
- using the rules for addition and subtraction of directed numbers
- using the rules for multiplication and division of directed numbers.

1 The lowest and highest temperatures ever recorded in the countries of the UK are shown in the table.

Country	Lowest temperature (°C)	Highest temperature (°C)
Northern Ireland	−17.5	30.8
England	−26.1	38.5
Wales	−23.3	33.6
Scotland	−27.2	32.9

Which of the countries has the biggest difference between their highest and lowest temperatures?

2 Calculate these.

  a $3 - 5$ **b** $-5 + 2$ **c** $7 - 15$ **d** $4 - 60$

  e $3 - 4 - 7$ **f** $-14 + 31$ **g** $-16 + 25$ **h** $-13 + 13$

  i $-40 + 17$ **j** $-2 + 10 - 17$ **k** $-24 - 48$ **l** $-72 + (-8)$

  m $-6 + (-25)$ **n** $16 - (-38)$ **o** $-15 - (-7)$ **p** $16 + (-49)$

  q $24 + (-37) - 15$ **r** $-8 - 19 - 36$ **s** $-13 + (-29) - (-18)$ **t** $-6 - 27 - (-82)$

  u $5 + (-61) - 29$ **v** $-42 - 42 - (-6)$ **w** $-11 - (-19) + (-30)$ **x** $-16 + (-17) - 28$

  y $-19 - (-34) - 67$

3 On Tuesday the temperature at midday was 6 °C.

  a By midnight it had dropped by 10 °C. What was the temperature at midnight?

  b At 6 a.m. the temperature was −1 °C. By how much had it changed since midnight?

4 Calculate these.

  a 2×0 **b** -5×8 **c** $-6 \times (-2)$ **d** -4×6

  e $5 \times (-7)$ **f** -3×7 **g** $-4 \times (-5)$ **h** $28 \div (-7)$

  i $-25 \div 5$ **j** $-20 \div 4$ **k** $(-8)^2 \div 4$ **l** $-15 \div (-3)$

  m $-35 \div 7$ **n** $64 \div (-8)$ **o** $27 \div (-9)$ **p** $3 \times 6 \div (-9)$

  q $-6 \times (-8) \div (-2)$ **r** $5 \times 6 \div (-10)$ **s** $-9 \times 4 \div (-6)$ **t** $-5 \times 6 \times (-4) \div (-8)$

5 Calculate these.

  a $(2 \times -3) + (4 \times -5)$ **b** $4 - (3 \times -2)$ **c** $5 - 3 - 2 + 6 - 5$

  d $(4 - 1) \times (5 + 3)$ **e** $\dfrac{4 \times (-6)}{2 + 6}$ **f** $-2 + (-3) - 4$

  g $-6 \times (-3) \div (-9) \times (-2)$ **h** $(-2 - 3) \div (-7 + 2)$ **i** $(-1 \times -3 \times -2) + (3 \times -5)$

  j $\dfrac{2 - 8 + 3}{-3 \times (-1)}$ **k** $(-3)^2 + (-2)^2$ **l** $(-2)^3 \times (-4)$

  m $-5 + 6 \times 3$ **n** $-2 + 20 \div 2$ **o** $\sqrt{4} - 3^2 - 2^3$

  p $\sqrt{25} - (-6)^2$ **q** $(-12 + 8 \div 2)^2$ **r** $(-3 + -2 - -1)^3$

CHAPTER 5 Fractions

This chapter is about

- recognising and using equivalent fractions
- converting between improper fractions and mixed numbers
- ordering fractions
- solving problems involving addition, subtraction, multiplication and division of fractions
- calculating a fraction of a quantity.

Exercise A

Do not use a calculator in these exercises.

1 Fill in the missing numbers for each pair of equivalent fractions.

    a $\dfrac{3}{4} = \dfrac{\square}{20}$ **b** $\dfrac{15}{21} = \dfrac{5}{\square}$ **c** $\dfrac{1}{2} = \dfrac{\square}{22}$ **d** $\dfrac{18}{60} = \dfrac{3}{\square}$ **e** $\dfrac{16}{18} = \dfrac{\square}{9}$

2 Write each fraction in its lowest terms.

    a $\dfrac{8}{10}$ **b** $\dfrac{15}{18}$ **c** $\dfrac{18}{24}$ **d** $\dfrac{14}{28}$

    e $\dfrac{9}{15}$ **f** $\dfrac{10}{30}$ **g** $\dfrac{25}{40}$ **h** $\dfrac{24}{32}$

    i $\dfrac{20}{55}$ **j** $\dfrac{18}{45}$ **k** $\dfrac{120}{200}$ **l** $\dfrac{54}{162}$

3 Put each set of fractions in order from smallest to largest.

    a $\dfrac{1}{4} \quad \dfrac{3}{10} \quad \dfrac{7}{20} \quad \dfrac{27}{100}$ **b** $\dfrac{3}{5} \quad \dfrac{2}{3} \quad \dfrac{5}{12} \quad \dfrac{13}{20}$

4 Change each of these improper fractions to a mixed number.

    a $\dfrac{7}{2}$ **b** $\dfrac{10}{3}$ **c** $\dfrac{17}{8}$ **d** $\dfrac{14}{9}$ **e** $\dfrac{19}{5}$

    f $\dfrac{10}{7}$ **g** $\dfrac{12}{7}$ **h** $\dfrac{11}{2}$ **i** $\dfrac{13}{4}$ **j** $\dfrac{11}{3}$

5 Change each of these mixed numbers to an improper fraction.

    a $1\dfrac{2}{7}$ **b** $1\dfrac{5}{8}$ **c** $7\dfrac{1}{2}$ **d** $2\dfrac{3}{4}$ **e** $3\dfrac{2}{5}$

    f $2\dfrac{4}{5}$ **g** $3\dfrac{2}{9}$ **h** $4\dfrac{5}{6}$ **i** $5\dfrac{1}{8}$ **j** $4\dfrac{1}{3}$

6 Write each of these in their simplest form (as fractions or mixed numbers).

    a $\dfrac{18}{10}$ **b** $\dfrac{15}{9}$ **c** $\dfrac{28}{24}$ **d** $\dfrac{7}{28}$ **e** $\dfrac{9}{6}$

    f $\dfrac{10}{28}$ **g** $\dfrac{25}{15}$ **h** $\dfrac{24}{18}$ **i** $\dfrac{65}{55}$ **j** $\dfrac{60}{45}$

Exercise B

1 Work out these.

a $\dfrac{1}{2} + \dfrac{2}{9}$ **b** $\dfrac{11}{12} - \dfrac{2}{3}$ **c** $\dfrac{5}{9} \times \dfrac{1}{10}$ **d** $\dfrac{2}{3} \div \dfrac{5}{6}$ **e** $\dfrac{1}{4} + \dfrac{2}{5} \times \dfrac{1}{3}$

2 Work out these.

a $4\dfrac{1}{4} + 3\dfrac{1}{3}$ **b** $6\dfrac{8}{9} + 1\dfrac{2}{3}$ **c** $5\dfrac{3}{8} - \dfrac{1}{4}$ **d** $5\dfrac{11}{16} - 2\dfrac{1}{8}$

e $4\dfrac{3}{4} + 3\dfrac{2}{7}$ **f** $6\dfrac{1}{4} - 2\dfrac{2}{3}$ **g** $7\dfrac{1}{9} - 2\dfrac{2}{3}$ **h** $5\dfrac{3}{10} - 4\dfrac{4}{5}$

3 Mary cut two pieces of wood, of lengths $3\dfrac{7}{8}$ inches and $7\dfrac{3}{4}$ inches, from a piece 18 inches long. What length of wood was left?

4 Work out these. Write your answers as simply as possible.

a $5\dfrac{1}{2} + 3\dfrac{5}{9} - 4\dfrac{2}{3}$ **b** $6\dfrac{2}{5} - 2\dfrac{7}{10} + 3\dfrac{1}{2}$ **c** $3\dfrac{2}{5} + 4\dfrac{7}{8} - 2\dfrac{3}{4}$

5 A shopkeeper had a roll of cloth $16\dfrac{1}{2}$ metres long. Anna bought a piece $2\dfrac{3}{4}$ metres long. How much was left?

6 A shopkeeper sells wire netting by the metre. He buys it in 10-metre rolls. Two customers buy $2\dfrac{2}{5}$ and $3\dfrac{1}{4}$ metres respectively. A third customer wants $4\dfrac{1}{2}$ metres. Will the shopkeeper need to start a new roll? Show your working.

7 Calculate these.

a $1\dfrac{1}{4} \times \dfrac{3}{5}$ **b** $2\dfrac{1}{2} \times 1\dfrac{3}{5}$ **c** $4\dfrac{1}{4} \times 2\dfrac{2}{5}$

d $3\dfrac{2}{3} \times 2\dfrac{1}{4}$ **e** $3\dfrac{1}{6} \times \dfrac{3}{5}$ **f** $4\dfrac{1}{5} \times 1\dfrac{3}{14}$

8 Calculate these.

a $3\dfrac{1}{4} \div 1\dfrac{1}{8}$ **b** $4\dfrac{1}{6} \div 1\dfrac{3}{7}$ **c** $6\dfrac{2}{5} \div \dfrac{8}{15}$

d $3\dfrac{1}{6} \div 1\dfrac{1}{9}$ **e** $2\dfrac{3}{4} \div 5\dfrac{1}{2}$ **f** $2\dfrac{2}{7} \div 3\dfrac{2}{3}$

9 Calculate these.

a $4\dfrac{1}{2} \times 2\dfrac{1}{6}$ **b** $5\dfrac{1}{4} \times 3\dfrac{1}{7}$ **c** $5\dfrac{3}{4} \div \dfrac{5}{8}$ **d** $8 \div 3\dfrac{1}{3}$ **e** $5\dfrac{1}{7} \times 1\dfrac{5}{9}$

f $1\dfrac{3}{5} \div 4\dfrac{1}{10}$ **g** $3\dfrac{5}{9} \times 2\dfrac{5}{8}$ **h** $4\dfrac{1}{6} \div 1\dfrac{2}{9}$ **i** $4\dfrac{2}{7} \times 1\dfrac{5}{16}$ **j** $3\dfrac{3}{4} \div 1\dfrac{5}{16}$

k $4\dfrac{1}{7} \div 1\dfrac{3}{14}$ **l** $5\dfrac{1}{3} \times 2\dfrac{5}{8}$ **m** $4\dfrac{3}{5} \div 5\dfrac{2}{3}$ **n** $2\dfrac{7}{10} \times 3\dfrac{2}{9}$ **o** $1\dfrac{4}{5} \div 3\dfrac{4}{9}$

10 Calculate these.

a $1\dfrac{3}{4} \times 2\dfrac{1}{2} \times \dfrac{8}{15}$ **b** $1\dfrac{1}{3} \times 3\dfrac{2}{5} \div 1\dfrac{5}{6}$ **c** $4\dfrac{2}{7} \times 2\dfrac{4}{5} \div 2\dfrac{1}{4}$

d $4\dfrac{1}{2} + 2\dfrac{1}{3} \times \dfrac{5}{14}$ **e** $5\dfrac{1}{4} - 2\dfrac{2}{3} \div 2\dfrac{2}{9}$ **f** $5\dfrac{1}{3} + 2\dfrac{3}{4} \div 3\dfrac{3}{10}$

Exercise C

1 Calculate these.

   a $\dfrac{3}{7}$ of 196   **b** $\dfrac{7}{8}$ of £192   **c** $\dfrac{3}{5}$ of 235 miles   **d** $\dfrac{4}{7}$ of £357.35

2 Which is larger, a $\dfrac{3}{8}$ share of £240 or a $\dfrac{3}{5}$ share of £150? Show your working.

3 Alan spent one-third of his pocket money on sweets and two-fifths on magazines. He saved the rest. What fraction did he save?

4 A farmer owns 400 animals. $\dfrac{3}{8}$ of them are pigs and $\dfrac{1}{4}$ of them are cows. The rest are sheep. How many sheep does the farmer own?

5 In 2010 a website had 230 000 hits. In 2011 the number of hits increased by $\dfrac{2}{5}$. In 2012 the number of hits decreased by $\dfrac{1}{4}$.
How many hits were there in 2012?

6 A girl spends $\dfrac{3}{5}$ of her pocket money on clothes. She spends $\dfrac{1}{4}$ of the rest on make-up. She has just enough money left to buy a book at £4.50.
How much pocket money did she have to start with?

7 Given that $\dfrac{p}{8}$ and $\dfrac{3}{q}$ are proper fractions and that $\dfrac{p}{8} \div \dfrac{3}{q} = \dfrac{5}{6}$, find possible values for p and q.

Exercise D

Work out these. Give your answer in its simplest form.

1 $\dfrac{x}{3} + \dfrac{x}{5}$ 2 $\dfrac{m}{2} - \dfrac{m}{3}$ 3 $\dfrac{5w}{8} + \dfrac{w}{5}$ 4 $\dfrac{9e}{10} - \dfrac{2e}{3}$

5 $\dfrac{c}{4} + \dfrac{d}{5}$ 6 $\dfrac{4m}{5} - \dfrac{2e}{7}$ 7 $\dfrac{x}{2} + \dfrac{x}{3} + \dfrac{y}{4}$ 8 $\dfrac{11y}{12} - \dfrac{5y}{6} + \dfrac{x}{3}$

9 $\dfrac{x}{4} \times \dfrac{x}{3} \times \dfrac{10}{y}$ 10 $\dfrac{x}{4} + \dfrac{x}{3} \times \dfrac{x}{2}$ 11 $\dfrac{x}{3} \times \dfrac{2}{x}$ 12 $\dfrac{m}{5} \times \dfrac{2}{m} \times \dfrac{x}{6}$

13 $\dfrac{w}{4} \div \dfrac{w}{5}$ 14 $\dfrac{c}{10} \div \dfrac{d}{3}$ 15 $\dfrac{x}{4} \div 8$ 16 $\dfrac{n}{2} \div y$

17 $\dfrac{x}{2} + \dfrac{x}{3} \div 7$ 18 $\dfrac{x}{5} \times \dfrac{x}{6} \div \dfrac{x}{4}$ 19 $\dfrac{5w}{4} \times \dfrac{2w}{15}$ 20 $\left(\dfrac{x}{4}\right)^2 \div \dfrac{m}{8}$

CHAPTER 6 Approximation and estimation

This chapter is about

- rounding a value correct to a given number of decimal places
- knowing the number of significant figures in any value
- rounding a value correct to a given number of significant figures
- estimating answers to practical problems, and using estimation as a check as to the appropriate size of the answer to a calculation.

1 Write each of these numbers
 i correct to 1 decimal place.
 ii correct to 2 decimal places.
 a 80.9346   b 5.1174   c 4.39852
 d 0.034 99   e 649.0019   f 16.984

2 Round each of these numbers to 1 significant figure.
 a 14.3   b 38   c 6.54   d 308   e 1210
 f 0.78   g 0.61   h 0.053   i 2413.5   j 0.0097
 k 8.4   l 18.36   m 725   n 8032   o 98.3
 p 0.71   q 0.0052   r 0.019   s 407.511   t 23 095

3 641 people attended a firework display. How many is this to 1 significant figure?

4 a Jenny measured a piece of wood as 2.84 m long. What is this to 1 significant figure?
 b Ben measured the wood as 284 cm. What is this to 1 significant figure?

5 Write each of these numbers to the given degree of accuracy.
 a 851 (1 s.f.)   b 568 790 (1 s.f.)   c 6.8 (1 s.f.)
 d 0.000 409 (1 s.f.)   e 18.6 (2 s.f.)   f 0.994 (2 s.f.)
 g 7.389 (3 s.f.)   h 2.718 282 (3 s.f.)   i 7.994 (2 s.f.)

6 Find an approximate answer to each of the calculations by rounding each number to 1 significant figure. Show your working.

 a $223.7 + 387.2$ b $791 \div 81.6$ c 18.2×53.7

 d 692^2 e $\dfrac{94.6}{37.7 \times 21.7}$ f 61.7×5.8

 g 3.7×9.1 h 23.127×28.4 i 73.4×46.8

 j $\dfrac{17.8 \times 5.7}{39.2}$ k $\sqrt{9.7 \times 11.2}$ l 0.82×27.3

 m $\dfrac{0.58 \times 73.4}{6.12}$ n 21.2^3 o 189×0.31

 p $\sqrt{11.1^2 - 8.4^2}$ q $\dfrac{51.8 + 39.2}{0.022}$ r 71×58

s $\dfrac{614.2}{0.49}$

t $\dfrac{5987}{5.1}$

u 19.1^2

v 62.7×8316

w $\dfrac{5.72}{19.3}$

x $\dfrac{32}{49.4}$

y 8152×37

z $\dfrac{935 \times 41}{8.5}$

In Questions 7 to 16, show the approximations that you use to get the estimates.

7 Estimate the answers to these calculations.

a 6.32×7.12 **b** $28.7 \div 6.3$

c 48.3×32.1 **d** $7896 \div 189$

e 286×0.32 **f** 18.9^2

g $913 \div 196$ **h** $4.7 \times 6.2 \times 9.8$

i $\dfrac{673 \times 0.76}{3.6 \times 2.38}$ **j** $\dfrac{8.94 \times 6.03}{0.53 - 0.29}$

8 Oisin bought 22 cans of drink at 39p each. Estimate what he paid in total.

9 Tickets for a firework display are £18.50 each. 4125 tickets are sold. Estimate the total value of the sales.

10 A rectangle measures 3.9 cm by 8.1 cm. Estimate its area.

11 A rectangle is 4.8 cm wide and its area is 32.1 cm^2.
   a Estimate the length of the rectangle.
   b Is the estimate smaller or bigger than the actual length? Explain your answer.

12 Sophie cut 2.9 m of ribbon into pieces 0.18 m long. Estimate how many pieces she had.

13 A café floor is 4.75 metres by 6.35 metres. The owner wants to cover the floor with tiles which cover 0.25 square metres each. Estimate the number of tiles needed.

14 A new computer is priced at £595 excluding VAT. VAT at 20% must be paid on it. Estimate the amount of VAT to be paid.

15 A square paving slab has an area of 6000 cm^2. Estimate the length of a side of the slab.

16 A circle has radius 4.3 cm. Estimate its area. ($\pi = 3.141\ldots$)

CHAPTER 7

The order of operations

This chapter is about

- applying the BODMAS rule to calculations involving several operations
- inserting the appropriate operations in order to make a calculation correct
- using the various functions on a calculator to evaluate answers
- planning and evaluating a detailed calculation on a calculator
- rounding to various degrees of accuracy appropriate to the context of the question.

Exercise A

Work out these.

1 $4 + 7 \times 2$

2 $3 \times 4 - 2$

3 $(12 - 3) \times 3$

4 $6 + 10 \div 2$

5 $8 \div 2 + 5 \times 3$

6 $3 \times 6 + 8 \div 2 \times 3$

7 $4 + 2(9 - 3 \times 2)$

8 $1.63 + 0.4 \times 1.2$

9 $(12 - 3 \times 2) + 2(18 \div 3 + 1)$

10 $2\frac{1}{4} + 3\frac{1}{2} \times \frac{1}{3}$

11 $\dfrac{16 - 8 \div 4}{5 + 2 \times 1}$

12 $\dfrac{4 + 3(10 + 4 \div 2)}{5 - 1 \times 3}$

Insert the appropriate operations to make each of these calculations correct. You may also insert brackets.

13 $26 \ \square \ 2 \ \square \ 4 = 17$

14 $6 \ \square \ 2 \ \square \ 3 = 15$

15 $18 \ \square \ 6 \ \square \ 2 = 21$

16 $19 \ \square \ 2 \ \square \ 3 = 13$

17 $5 \ \square \ 3 \ \square \ 4 \ \square \ 5 = 35$

18 $6 \ \square \ 5 \ \square \ 1 \ \square \ 2 = 9$

19 $3 \ \square \ 8 \ \square \ 2 \ \square \ 1 = 11$

20 $10 \ \square \ 2 \ \square \ 6 \ \square \ 3 = 5$

Exercise B

Use your calculator to work out each of these.

1 $9.6 - 1.85$

2 3.2^3

3 $4 + (-3) - (-9)$

4 $\dfrac{3.2}{4} + 0.85$

5 $\sqrt{2.56}$

6 $4.25 + 0.95 - 0.05^2$

7 $\dfrac{8 + 2^3}{0.4^2}$

8 $\sqrt[4]{20\,736}$

9 $13\frac{2}{3} - 1\frac{1}{2} \times 4\frac{3}{4}$

10 $15^3 - 6^2 + 2^6$

Exercise C

Use a calculator to work out these. Give your answers either exactly or to 2 decimal places.

1 $-2.7 + 3.8 - 4.9 + 2.1$

2 $-2.1 \times 4.2 + 2.7 \times (-4.6)$

3 $\dfrac{4.6 - 3.7}{9 - 7.4}$

4 $\dfrac{-2.7 \times 3.9}{2.6 + 3.7}$

5 $\dfrac{9.2}{1.3 + 5.4}$

6 $\dfrac{18.4 - 9.1}{3.8}$

7 $\dfrac{10}{0.56 - 0.32}$

8 $\dfrac{6.7 + 9.3}{8.4 \times 4.9}$

9 $(43.7 - 18.4) \div 3.6$

10 $\dfrac{16.7 \times 5.2}{6.1 \times 0.36}$

Work out these on your calculator. If the answers are not exact, give them correct to 3 decimal places.

11 3.2^4

12 $\sqrt{2^2 - 1.8^2}$

13 $2.3 \times 4.7^2 - 4.6 \div 2.89$

14 $\sqrt{17.3 + 16.8}$

15 $\sqrt{68.7 - 2.3^2}$

16 $(7.3 - 2.6)^2$

17 $7.3^2 - 2.6^2$

18 $5.8 \times (1.9 + 7.3)^2$

19 $\sqrt{28.6 - 9.7}$

20 $\sqrt{\dfrac{26.2}{3.8}}$

Work these out on your calculator. Give answers correct to 3 significant figures.

21 $\sqrt[3]{\dfrac{8.6^2 \times 1.3}{2.9}}$

22 $\dfrac{6}{1.3^2} + \dfrac{2}{0.5^2}$

23 $\dfrac{11.6}{9.1} \times 2.3 + 5.4$

24 $\dfrac{6.1 + 9.3 \times 2}{\sqrt{5.6 - 1.3^2}}$

25 $\dfrac{8.21 + \sqrt{2.6^3}}{5.1 + 2.3 \times 1.7^4}$

26 A rectangle is 8.4 cm by 3.2 cm. Work out the area.

27 A square has a side of 6.23 cm. Work out the area.

28 Sarah typed 12 341 words. She is paid 0.64 pence per word. How much does she earn?

CHAPTER 8

Ratio

This chapter is about
- simplifying ratios
- dividing in a given ratio
- using ratios in context, for solving problems.

Exercise A

1 Write each of these ratios in its simplest form.
  a $8:6$ **b** $20:50$ **c** $35:55$ **d** $8:24:32$ **e** $15:25:20$

2 Write each of these ratios in its simplest form.
  a $200\,g:500\,g$ **b** $60p:£3$ **c** 1 minute : 25 seconds   **d** $2\,m:80\,cm$

  e $500\,g:3\,kg$ **f** $£1.60:£2.40$ **g** $\dfrac{3}{4}:\dfrac{7}{8}$ **h** $2\dfrac{5}{8}:1\dfrac{5}{6}$

3 Write each of these ratios in the form $1:n$.
  a $2:10$ **b** $5:30$ **c** $2:9$ **d** $4:9$ **e** $50\,g:30\,g$

  f $15p:£3$ **g** $25\,cm:6\,m$ **h** $20:7$ **i** $4\,cm:1\,km$ **j** $\dfrac{1}{4}\,km:2\,km$

4 Terry, Janine and Abigail receive £200, £350 and £450 respectively as their dividends in a joint investment. Write the ratio of their dividends in its simplest form.

5 Three saucepans hold 500 ml, 1 litre and 2.5 litres respectively. Write the ratio of their capacities in its simplest form.

6 Share £40 between Paula and Tom in the ratio $3:5$.

7 Split £1950 in the ratio $4:5:6$.

8 Sue, Jane and Christine invest £70 000 between them in the ratio $2:3:5$. How much do they each invest?

9 Grey paint is made with 2 parts white to 3 parts black. How much black is needed to make 2.5 litres of grey?

10 A metal alloy is made up of copper, iron and nickel in the ratio $3:4:2$. How much of each metal is there in 450 g of the alloy?

11 Hollie spends her pocket money on sweets, magazines and clothes in the ratio $2:3:7$. She receives £15 a week. How much does she spend on sweets?

12 In an election the number of votes was shared between the Labour, Conservative and other parties in the ratio $5:4:2$. Labour received 7500 votes.
  a How many votes did the Conservatives receive?
  b How many votes did the other parties receive?

13 A woman shares her inheritance among herself and her 2 daughters in the ratio $3:1:1$. One of the daughters then shares her money with her son in the ratio $3:2$. If the inheritance was £160 000; how much does the son get?

Exercise B

1 On a map a distance of 12 mm represents a distance of 3 km on the ground. What is the scale of the map in the form 1 : n?

2 To make mortar, Fred mixes 1 part cement with 5 parts sand.
   a How much sand does he mix with 500 g of cement?
   b How much cement does he mix with 4.5 kg of sand?

3 Callum uses blue and white tiles in the ratio 1 : 6 to decorate his bathroom.
   a He uses twelve blue tiles on the side of the bath. How many white tiles does he use?
   b He uses 240 white tiles in the shower. How many blue tiles does he use?

4 A plan of a forest is drawn using a scale of 2 centimetres to 50 metres.
   a On the plan, the forest is 24 cm wide. What is the actual width of the forest?
   b The actual length of the forest is 950 m. What is the length of the forest on the plan?

5 Two photographs are in the ratio 3 to 4.
   a The smaller photograph is 9 cm long. How long is the larger photograph?
   b The larger photograph is 8.4 cm wide. How wide is the smaller photograph?

6 A model of a theatre set is made on a scale of 1 to 20.
   a A rug on the set is 120 cm long. How long is it on the model?
   b A cupboard on the model is 9 cm high. How high is it on the set?

7 Michael has a recipe for Twinkie Crackle that makes enough for eight people. The recipe uses 200 g of Twinkies.
   a What mass of Twinkies does Michael need to make enough Twinkie Crackle for six people?
   b Michael has 325 g of Twinkies. How many people can he make Twinkie Crackle for?

8 A map is drawn to a scale of 1 : 40 000.
   a Calculate the length of a road which is 6.5 cm on the map.
   b Two villages are 5 km apart. How far apart will they appear on the map?

9 The ratio of pens to pencils in my pencil case is 5 : 3. If I have 9 pencils, what is the total number of pens and pencils in my pencil case?

10 $\frac{2}{5}$ of a school are boys. If there are 468 girls, how many pupils are there in total?

CHAPTER 9

Percentages and finance

This chapter is about

- knowing the meaning of a percentage
- converting between percentages, fractions, decimals and ratios
- finding a percentage of a quantity, both with and without a calculator
- increasing or decreasing a quantity by a given percentage
- finding one number as a percentage of another
- knowing the formula for percentage change, and applying it in various contexts
- using reverse percentages to calculate an original value
- understanding the concept of simple interest and compound interest and solving a variety of problems
- using percentages and other techniques for solving a variety of finance type problems.

Exercise A

1 Change each of these percentages to **i** a fraction and **ii** a decimal.
   a 45%   **b** 75%   **c** 12%   **d** 110%   **e** 9%   **f** 17.5%

2 Change each of these decimals to **i** a percentage and **ii** a fraction.
   a 0.47   **b** 0.82   **c** 0.04   **d** 0.425   **e** 1.35   **f** $0.\dot{3}$

3 Change each of these fractions to **i** a decimal and **ii** a percentage.
   a $\frac{19}{100}$ **b** $\frac{9}{50}$ **c** $\frac{13}{20}$ **d** $\frac{3}{100}$ **e** $\frac{7}{4}$ **f** $\frac{3}{11}$

4 Put these in order, smallest first.

   a $\frac{29}{100}$, 0.3, 0.32, 31%, $\frac{1}{3}$

   b 0.25, $\frac{3}{10}$, 0.35, 0.27, 28%

   c 0.46, $\frac{64}{100}$, 0.65, $\frac{9}{20}$, 56%

   d $\frac{7}{10}$, $\frac{17}{25}$, 72%, 0.84, $\frac{2}{3}$

   e $\frac{1}{3}$, $\frac{7}{25}$, 30%, 0.29, 16.9%

   f 0.605, $\frac{2}{3}$, 66%, $\frac{7}{9}$, 0.67

5 At Tony's school, $\frac{8}{25}$ of the students support Man. Utd. 27% support Man. City. Which team has the higher support at Tony's school and by how much?

6 Express $\frac{43}{125}$ as an exact decimal.

7 The ratio of boys to girls in a school is 3 : 5. What percentage are girls?

8 Find $0.01 \times 0.03 \times 0.05$ as a fraction in its lowest terms.

9 Find
  a 30% of £7.20
  b 15% of £40
  c 45% of £240

10 65% of the 840 students in a school eat in the cafeteria. How many students do not?

11 A television normally costs £400. In a sale, the shopkeeper decides to reduce the price by 10% each week until it is sold.
The television is sold during the third week. What price does the television sell for?

12 Work out
  a 37.5% of 6.72m
  b 17% of £6300
  c 27% of £12

13 Increase £600 by each of these percentages.
  a 10%   **b** 15%   **c** 2%   **d** 9.5%

14 Decrease £400 by each of these percentages.
  a 25%   **b** 18%   **c** 6%   **d** 11%

15 A shop reduced all its prices by 12%. A coat originally cost £60. What is the new price?

16 Damien earns £15 000 per year. He receives a salary increase of 3.5%. Find his new salary.

17 A shop reduced its prices by 12% in a sale.
On the final day of the sale, there was also a discount of 25% off the sale prices. On the final day, Katie bought a skirt which was originally priced at £36.
How much did she pay for it?

18 A metal bar is 583mm long. When heated its length increases by 0.12%. Find its new length.

Exercise B

For percentages, give your answer either exactly or to 1 decimal place.

1 Find these.
  a 6m as a fraction of 75m   **b** £3.80 as a fraction of £5   **c** 28 as a percentage of 100
  d 18 as a percentage of 150   **e** £572 as a percentage of £880   **f** 60cm as a percentage of 2.5m

2 For each of these, write the first quantity as a percentage of the second.
  a 14 and 100   **b** 6 and 50   **c** 3m and 5m   **d** 27p and £1   **e** £1.20 and £5
  f 14 and 84   **g** 6 and 35   **h** 2m and 9m   **i** 27p and 90p   **j** £1.47 and £3.75

3 There are 350 people in a cinema audience. 139 of them are under eighteen.
What percentage is this?

4 At a tennis club the membership consists of 85 women and 63 men. What percentage of the members are women?

5 What percentage of 3.5kg is 450g?

6 A car was bought for £9000. A year later it was sold for £7500. Find the % loss.

7 A girl invests £6000 in a bank account. One year later, there is £6240 in the account. What is the % interest rate per annum?

8 A rectangle 24m by 18m has both its length and width increased by 5%.
What is the exact % increase in its area?

Percentages and finance   17

Exercise C

1 Barbara was given a 3.5% pay rise. Her salary is now £25 378.20 a year. What was her salary before the rise?

2 In a sale, everything is reduced by 30%.
A pair of trousers now costs £31.50. What was the price before the sale?

3 A watch is priced at £1692 including VAT at 17.5%. What is the cost without VAT?

4 The value of a car has fallen by 30% of its value when new. It is now worth £9450. How much did it cost when new?

5 The population of a country went up by 15% between 1995 and 2010.
The population in 2010 was 32.2 million. What was the population in 1995?

6 The value of a company's shares fell by 78%.
The value of a share is now £1.32. What was the value before the fall?

7 Electricity prices increased by 66% in 2009. Mr and Mrs Smith's average monthly bill was £69.72 after the increase. What was their average bill before the increase?

8 A train company offers a 40% reduction for travelling at off-peak times.
An off-peak ticket costs £45. What is the full price of a ticket?

9 House prices in a certain area went up by 150% between 1995 and 2005. The price of a house in the area was £180 000 in 2005. What was the price in 1995?

10 A coat is reduced by 15% in the first week of a sale and by a further 10% of the sale price in the second week of the sale. The sale price the second week is £68.85. Calculate the original price of the coat.

Exercise D

1   David is buying a sound system. It will need to be installed. He sees these two adverts for the same sound system.

Sounds Rite	Cheaper Sounds
Cash	**Cash**
£1199 + VAT at 20%	£1350
Free Installation	Installation £40
Or easy terms	**Or easy terms**
Pay £500 deposit	20% deposit
+	+
12 monthly payments of £85	12 monthly payments of £99

Which company is cheaper for David and by how much if
  a   he is paying cash?
  b   he is paying by easy terms?

2 A colony of rabbits increases by 15% each year. This year there are 250 rabbits. How many will there be in 3 years' time?

3 Mr Brown has £10000 to invest for 4 years. He can invest it at a simple interest rate of 6.5 % p.a. or at a compound interest rate of 5.25 % p.a. Which will give him more interest and by how much?

4 The value of a caravan falls by 18% a year. A caravan costs £10350 new. How much is it worth after 2 years? Give your answer to the nearest pound.

5 The value of a car reduces by 11% per year.
It cost £18000 new. How many years will it take to reduce in value below £10000?

6 Is it better to invest £2000 for 6 years at 4.5% or for 5 years at 5%? Both pay compound interest annually.

7 Naomi has £5000 to invest. She is looking at these two accounts. They both pay compound interest annually.

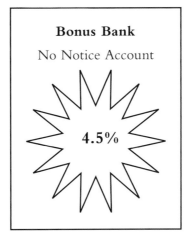

| **Anglo Bank** |
| No Notice Account. |
| **4.75%**★★ |
| ★★**Introductory offer.** |
| Reduces to 4.25% after 1 year. |

Bonus Bank

No Notice Account

4.5%

Which bank pays more interest over a 3-year investment and by how much?

8 A car depreciates by 12% per year. How many years does it take for the car to halve its value?

9 A motorbike depreciates in value by 5% every year. After 3 years it is worth £5487.20. Calculate its original value.

10 A girl spends $120 on a handbag whilst on holiday. She sees the same handbag later priced at €115. What was her % saving?
£1 = €1.15
£1 = $1.50

This chapter is about

- finding a reciprocal by writing the value as a fraction in the form $\frac{a}{b}$ and inverting
- knowing the properties of reciprocals
- knowing the calculator function for a reciprocal.

1 Write down the reciprocal of each of these numbers.
  a 3   **b** 6   **c** 640   **d** −10   **e** −317

2 Write down the numbers of which these are the reciprocals.
  a $\frac{1}{18}$ **b** $\frac{1}{52}$ **c** $\frac{1}{1000}$ **d** $\frac{2}{5}$ **e** $-\frac{1}{2}$

3 Find the reciprocal of each of these numbers, giving your answer as a fraction or a mixed number.
  a $\frac{4}{5}$ **b** $\frac{3}{8}$ **c** $1\frac{3}{5}$ **d** $3\frac{1}{3}$ **e** $\frac{2}{25}$

4 Calculate the reciprocal of each of these.
  a 2.5   **b** 0.2   **c** 1.25   **d** 0.16   **e** 3.2

5 Write down the reciprocal of each of these.
  a $\frac{a}{b}$ **b** y **c** $\frac{1}{p^2}$ **d** $\frac{-2x}{3}$ **e** $\left(n+\frac{1}{n}\right)$

6 What fraction does $1\frac{4}{5}$ need to be multiplied by to give an answer of 1?

7 Use the reciprocal function on your calculator to find the reciprocal of

  a 1.6

  b $\frac{5}{8}$

  c 4.5^2

  d 2.4^3 (3 s.f.)

  e 0.002

8 a Which number has no reciprocal?

  b Find b given that $3\frac{3}{4} \times b = 1$

  c $p > q$ then the reciprocal of $p >$ reciprocal of q. Is this statement true or false? Explain fully.

  d Find e given that $0.4 \times 2\frac{1}{2} + 0.3 \times 3\frac{1}{3} = e$

  e Find y given that $(1.6y)^2 = 1$

CHAPTER 11

Standard form

This chapter is about

- writing numbers in standard form
- converting numbers from standard form into decimal form
- adding, subtracting, multiplying and dividing numbers in standard form without a calculator
- using standard form on a calculator
- solving a variety of problems using standard form in context.

Exercise A

1 Write these numbers in standard form.
  a 40 000   **b** 4800   **c** 737 000   **d** 25
  e 8 000 000   **f** 12 340   **g** 6 million   **h** 78 900 000
  i 3.6 million   **j** 93 million   **k** $\frac{1}{2}$ million   **l** 2 000 000 000 000

2 Write these numbers in standard form.
  a 0.007   **b** 0.204   **c** 0.000 045   **d** 0.007 07
  e 0.000 000 1   **f** 0.079 36   **g** 0.100 08   **h** 0.000 647
  i $\frac{3}{1000}$ **j** $\frac{29}{10000}$ **k** 0.000 000 000 052   **l** $\frac{73}{1000000}$

3 These numbers are in standard form. Write them as ordinary numbers.
  a 3×10^4 **b** 5.7×10^6 **c** 8.75×10^{-1} **d** 4.02×10^{-3} **e** 7.73×10^2
  f 1.2×10^{-6} **g** 8.03×10^{10} **h** 5.48×10^5 **i** 9.99×10^{-2} **j** 3.86×10^{-4}

4 One trillion is one million million. Write this in standard form.

5 The mass of an oxygen atom is 2.73×10^{-20} mg. If this was written as a decimal, how many zeroes would there be between the decimal point and the 2?

6 Put these numbers in order from smallest to largest.
  1.26×10^{-3} 216×10^{-1} 2.16×10^2 1.62×10^{-1} 6.12×10^0

Exercise B

Work out these, without a calculator. Give your answers in standard form.

1 $(4.12 \times 10^2) + (3.4 \times 10^6)$

2 $(3.7 \times 10^{-3}) + (5.1 \times 10^{-2})$

3 $(8.3 \times 10^5) - (1.75 \times 10^3)$

4 $(6.14 \times 10^{-2}) - (5.3 \times 10^{-4})$

5 $(7.3 \times 10^6) - (6.4 \times 10^5)$

6 $(3.7 \times 10^{-2}) + (4.2 \times 10^{-3})$

7 $(8 \times 10^4) \times (4 \times 10^6)$

8 $(6 \times 10^8) \div (3 \times 10^3)$

9 $(1.5 \times 10^{-2}) \times (2 \times 10^{-3})$

10 $(1.5 \times 10^2) \div (5 \times 10^{-2})$

11 $(6.8 \times 10^{-5}) \div (2 \times 10^{-2})$

12 $(4.96 \times 10^{-3}) \times (6.1 \times 10^6)$

13 Calculate 8 million times 400 000.

14 A sheet of paper is 9.6×10^{-3} cm thick. How thick will a ream of paper be in mm? (ream = 500 sheets)

15 A particle has a mass 6.2×10^{-24} g. Find the total mass of 4 million particles.

16 A rectangle is 2.3×10^3 mm long and 1.4×10^2 mm wide. Calculate its perimeter.

Exercise C

You may use a calculator for these questions.

1 Work out these. Give your answers in standard form.
  a $(2.7 \times 10^2) \times (1.6 \times 10^6)$ **b** $(9.87 \times 10^6) \div (4.7 \times 10^4)$
  c $(6.8 \times 10^{-5}) \times (4.3 \times 10^3)$ **d** $(6.5 \times 10^{-2}) \times (8.9 \times 10^{-4})$
  e $(4.088 \times 10^5) \div (5.6 \times 10^{-2})$ **f** $(4.324 \times 10^{-4}) \div (4.7 \times 10^6)$
  g $(1.7 \times 10^{-2})^2$ **h** $(8.8 \times 10^6)^2$
  i $(3.27 \times 10^{-2}) - (8.16 \times 10^{-4})$ **j** $(7.26 \times 10^8) + (4.81 \times 10^6)$
  k $(1.44 \times 10^{-5}) + (3.75 \times 10^{-6})$ **l** $(3.7 \times 10^{-4}) - (4.81 \times 10^{-3})$

2 Work out these. Give your answers in standard form correct to 3 significant figures.
  a $(7.26 \times 10^4) \times (8.92 \times 10^6)$ **b** $(2.73 \times 10^8) \div (7.89 \times 10^3)$
  c $(9.15 \times 10^{-3}) \div (5.28 \times 10^4)$ **d** $(4.832 \times 10^{-6}) \times (7.021 \times 10^5)$
  e $(1.79 \times 10^5)^2$ **f** $\sqrt{5.2 \times 10^{12}}$

3 Work out these. Give your answers in standard form
  a $320\,000 \times 460\,000$ **b** $37\,200\,000 + 1\,800\,000$
  c $0.000\,0062 - 0.000\,005\,12$ **d** $46\,000\,000 \div 200\,000$
  e $0.000\,32 \times 41\,000$ **f** $(234\,000)^2$

4 There are 8.64×10^4 seconds in a day. There are 3.6525×10^4 days in a century.
  a How many seconds are there in a century? Give your answer in standard form correct to 3 significant figures.
  b What fraction of a century is a second? Give your answer as a decimal in standard form correct to 3 significant figures.

5 6000 hydrogen atoms weigh 1.002×10^{-23} kg. Find the mass of one atom in grams.

6 Light travels at a speed of 186 000 miles per second. How far will it travel in a year (365 days)? Give your answer in standard form, correct to 2 significant figures.

CHAPTER 12

Rational and irrational numbers

This chapter is about

- distinguishing between a rational and an irrational number
- writing all rational numbers as fractions of the form $\dfrac{a}{b}$
- solving problems involving rational and irrational numbers in context
- changing a recurring decimal to a fraction.

1 Decide whether each of these values is rational or irrational, giving reasons for your answers.

   a   0.1   **b**   0.123   **c** $\dfrac{5\pi}{2}$

   d   0.54   **e** $\sqrt{144}$ **f** $\sqrt{66}$

   g $5 \div 2\sqrt{3}$ **h** $\dfrac{5}{6}$ **i** $0.\dot{8}$

2 Decide whether each of these values is rational or irrational, giving reasons for your answers. For those that are rational, write them in the form $\dfrac{a}{b}$ in their lowest terms.

   a   0.56   **b** $0.\dot{5}\dot{6}$ **c** $\dfrac{3}{11}$

   d $\sqrt{24}$ **e** $\sqrt{25}$ **f** $\dfrac{4}{91}$

   g $\sqrt{121}$ **h** $\sqrt{8}$ **i** $0.10\dot{3}$

   j $3 + 7\pi$ **k** $16 - \sqrt{12}$

3 Convert these recurring decimals to fractions or mixed numbers in their lowest terms.

   a $0.\dot{7}\dot{2}$ **b** $0.4\dot{8}$ **c** $0.\dot{3}0\dot{6}$

   d $0.\dot{1}2\dot{3}$ **e** $1.\dot{2}\dot{7}$ **f** $1.3\dot{8}$

   g $0.6\dot{1}\dot{2}$ **h** $0.5\dot{6}$ **i** $0.3\dot{1}6\dot{2}$

4 **a**   Write down three different irrational numbers.

     b   Write down two irrational numbers that have a difference of 5.

5 For each of these numbers, find an irrational number which can be multiplied by it to give a rational result.

   a $\dfrac{5}{\sqrt{3}}$

   b $\dfrac{\pi}{6}$

   c $5\sqrt{7}$

6 Find two different irrational numbers whose product is rational.

7 Find an irrational number N such that N^2 is rational.

8 For the isosceles, right-angled triangle shown, state whether each of these are rational or irrational.

   a   sin 45
   b   cos 45
   c   tan 45

9 Write down two irrational numbers between 6 and 7.

10 Write down a rational number between $\sqrt{14}$ and $\sqrt{18}$.

This chapter is about

- simplifying surds using square numbers
- knowing and applying the rules of surds

$$\sqrt{a} \times \sqrt{a} = a$$

$$\sqrt{a} \times \sqrt{b} = \sqrt{ab}$$

$$\frac{\sqrt{a}}{\sqrt{b}} = \sqrt{\frac{a}{b}}$$

$$a\sqrt{b} \pm c\sqrt{b} = (a \pm c)\sqrt{b}$$

- rationalising the denominator of a surd.

Simplify each of these.

1 $\sqrt{28}$

2 $\sqrt{63}$

3 $\sqrt{125}$

4 $\sqrt{600}$

5 $3\sqrt{40}$

6 $4\sqrt{50}$

7 $2\sqrt{216}$

8 $3\sqrt{112}$

9 $\dfrac{\sqrt{108}}{3}$

10 $\dfrac{\sqrt{50}}{5}$

11 Simplify each of these.

  a $\sqrt{8} \times \sqrt{50}$

  b $\sqrt{75} \div \sqrt{27}$

  c $\sqrt{32} \times \sqrt{8}$

  d $\sqrt{15} \times \sqrt{27}$

  e $\dfrac{\sqrt{15}}{\sqrt{27}}$

  f $\dfrac{\sqrt{10} \times \sqrt{12}}{\sqrt{15}}$

12 Simplify each of these as far as possible.

  a $\sqrt{18} + \sqrt{72}$

  b $4\sqrt{3} + \sqrt{12}$

  c $5\sqrt{50} + 2\sqrt{8}$

  d $\sqrt{80} - \sqrt{5}$

  e $\sqrt{75} + \sqrt{27}$

  f $6\sqrt{8} - 5\sqrt{2}$

13 If $x = 5 + \sqrt{2}$ and $y = 5 - \sqrt{2}$, simplify these.

  a $x + y$

  b $x - y$

  c xy

14 If $x = 7 + \sqrt{3}$ and $y = 5 - 2\sqrt{3}$, simplify these.

  a $x + y$

  b $x - y$

  c x^2

  d xy

15 Expand and simplify these.

  a $(\sqrt{3} + 5)^2$

  b $(2 - \sqrt{3})(2 + \sqrt{3})$

  c $(6 - 2\sqrt{3})^2$

  d $(2\sqrt{7} + 5)(3\sqrt{7} - 2)$

16 Find the exact value of x, expressing your answer as simply as possible.

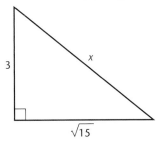

17 A square has sides of $\sqrt{8}$ cm.
  a Calculate the exact length of the diagonal, in its simplest form.
  b Calculate the exact perimeter, in its simplest form.
  c Calculate the exact area, in its simplest form.

18 Simplify each of these by rationalising the denominator.

  a $\dfrac{1}{\sqrt{3}}$ **b** $\dfrac{3}{\sqrt{5}}$

  c $\dfrac{7}{\sqrt{10}}$ **d** $\dfrac{10}{\sqrt{5}}$

  e $\dfrac{5}{2\sqrt{3}}$ **f** $\dfrac{1}{3\sqrt{2}}$

  g $\dfrac{\sqrt{3}}{3\sqrt{2}}$ **h** $\dfrac{7\sqrt{5}}{5\sqrt{7}}$

19 Simplify as far as possible $\dfrac{\sqrt{6}}{10} + \dfrac{2}{\sqrt{6}}$

20 Simplify as far as possible $\sqrt{50} - \dfrac{1}{\sqrt{2}}$

21 Which of the following are true and which are false?

  a $\sqrt{6} + \sqrt{6} = \sqrt{12}$

  b $\dfrac{\sqrt{8}}{2} = \sqrt{2}$

  c $\sqrt{7} \times \sqrt{7} = 7$

  d $3\sqrt{18} = \dfrac{18}{\sqrt{2}}$

  e $(3\sqrt{2} + 2\sqrt{3})^2 = 6(5 + \sqrt{6})$

CHAPTER 14

Algebra review

This chapter is about

- forming an algebraic expression for given information
- simplifying algebraic expressions by gathering like terms
- evaluating algebraic expressions by substituting in various numerical values.

Exercise A

Simplify the expressions in 1 to 30.

1 $a + a + a + a$

2 $2 \times a$

3 $a \times b \times c$

4 $y \times y$

5 $p + p + p + r + r + r + r$

6 $c + c + c - c$

7 $x + x + y + x + y + x + y + y + x$

8 $2a + 3b + 5a - b$

9 $4a - 2b + 3b$

10 $2 \times y + 3 \times s$

11 $a \times a \times a \times b \times b$

12 $4x \times 3y$

13 $8x + 3y + 2x - 3y$

14 $5ab + 3ac - 2ab$

15 $2a \times 3b$

16 $5x + 3y - 2x - y$

17 $3a + 2b + 3c + b + 3a - 3c$

18 $3a + 5b - 2a - 3b$

19 $5a^2 + 3a - 3a^2 + 6a$

20 $6p + 2q - 3 - 2p - 5q + 7$

21 $7p + 3q - 2p - 2q$

22 $3x^2 - x + 4x^2 + 5x - 2x^2 - 7x$

23 $5x^3 - 3x^2 + 2x$

24 $3ab - 2ac - ab + 5ac$

25 $3x - 2y + 4z - 2x - 3y + 5z + 6x + 2y - 3z$

26 $3a^2 - 3ab - 2ab + 4b^2$

27 $3a + 2b + 3c + b + 3a - 3c$

28 $1 + a + 2 - b + 3 + c$

29 $6ab + 3ac - 2ab + 5ab + 3ac$

30 $a^2 - 3ab - 3a^2 + 6ab - 2ab$

31 Thomas bought 6 packets of sweets at a pence each and 2 chocolate bars at $2a$ pence each. Find and simplify an expression for the total amount he spent in pence.

32 A shape is made up of a square of side a, a rectangle of sides $2a$ and $3a$ and a rectangle of sides $3a$ and b. All measurements are in cm. Find and simplify an expression for the total area of the complete shape.

33 If x is the largest of three consecutive even numbers, write an expression for the total of the three numbers in terms of x.

34 What must be added to each of these expressions to make $2a - b$?
i $a - 4b$
ii $5a + 2b$
iii $-a - b + 6$

Exercise B

1 Find the value of these expressions when $a = 4$ and $b = 2$.

a $a + b$ b $a - b$

c $2a$ d $7a$

e $5b$ f $8b$

g ab h a^2

i $3ab$ j $2a + b$

k $3a - b$ l $5a + 4b$

m $3a - 4b$ n $a^2 - b^2$

o $3a^2$ p $6b^2$

q a^2b r b^3

s $\dfrac{a}{b}$ t $\dfrac{10b}{a}$

u $b - a$ v $\dfrac{4b}{2a}$

w $\dfrac{a^2}{b^2}$ x $\dfrac{b}{a}$

y $2a^2$ z $(2a)^2$

2 Work out the value of $5t + 2$ when

a $t = 2$

b $t = 8$

c $t = -12$

d $t = 20$

e $t = \dfrac{1}{2}$

3 Work out the value of $2C - F$ when

a $C = 4$, $F = 4$

b $C = 3$, $F = -5$

c $C = -8$, $F = -3$

d $C = 0$, $F = 7$

4 Work out the value of $w + nd$ when

a $w = 1$, $n = 2$, $d = 1$

b $w = 4$, $n = 2$, $d = -6$

c $w = 12$, $n = 10$, $d = 0$

d $w = 50$, $n = -30$, $d = -10$

e $w = -11$, $n = 9$, $d = \dfrac{1}{2}$

5 Find the value of these expressions when $k = 3$ and $m = 2$.

a $2k + 5m$

b $3k - 10m$

c $3km - 4k^2$

d $2m^2k - 3km^2$

e $(2m + 3k)^2 - 2m^2k^2$

6 Evaluate each of these expressions for the values given.

a $4y - 5x$ when $y = 7$ and $x = -2$

b $fh + \dfrac{g}{h}$ when $f = 1.2$, $g = 3.5$ and $h = 0.5$

c $a^2 - c^3$ when $a = -5$ and $c = -3$

d $\dfrac{a}{2bc}$ when $a = 6$, $b = \dfrac{3}{4}$ and $c = -2$

e $mx^2 + c$ when $m = 3$, $x = -12$ and $c = 6$

7 Given that $p = \dfrac{1}{2}$, $q = 10$, $r = -2$ and $s = 5$ find the value of $\dfrac{pq(s - 5r)}{pqs}$.

8 Given that $a = -4$, $b = 2$, $c = -1$ and $d = -10$ find the value of $\dfrac{a^2c\,(d - 2c)}{-4(5b + 2c)}$.

This chapter is about

- knowing the rules for indices
- simplifying algebraic indices
- evaluating numerical indices
- solving index equations.

Exercise A

1 Write these in a simpler form, using indices.
- **a** $2 \times 2 \times 2 \times 2$
- **b** $2 \times 2 \times 3 \times 3 \times 5 \times 5 \times 5$
- **c** $a \times a \times a \times a \times a$

2 Write these in a simpler form, using indices.
- **a** $2^6 \times 2^5$
- **b** $3^6 \times 3^2$
- **c** $4^2 \times 4^3$
- **d** $5^6 \times 5$

3 Write these in a simpler form, using indices.
- **a** $5^5 \div 5^2$
- **b** $7^8 \div 7^2$
- **c** $2^6 \div 2^4$
- **d** $3^7 \div 3^3$

4 Write each of these expressions as a power of a single base number.
- **a** $\dfrac{2^5 \times 2^4}{2^3}$
- **b** $\dfrac{3^7}{3^5 \times 3^2}$
- **c** $\dfrac{5^5 \times 5^4}{5^2 \times 5^3}$
- **d** $\dfrac{7^5 \times 7^2}{7^2 \times 7^4}$
- **e** $\dfrac{125 \times 5^2}{5^3 \times 625}$
- **f** $\dfrac{3^6 \times 27}{9 \times 3^4}$

5 Simplify these.
- **a** $a^4 \times 2a^2$
- **b** $a^5 \div a^3$
- **c** $3a^3 \times 4a^2$
- **d** $12a^3 \div 4a^2$
- **e** $p^{-6} \times p^2$
- **f** $y^{1.5} \div y^{0.5}$
- **g** $k^{\frac{1}{5}} \times k^{\frac{-1}{2}}$
- **h** $\sqrt{t^4}$
- **i** $\dfrac{x}{\sqrt{x} \times \sqrt{x}}$
- **j** $6y^3 \times y^{-5}$
- **k** $(4a^2)^3$
- **l** $(6p^2q^3)^2$

6 Simplify where possible.
- **a** $2a^3 \times 3a^2$
- **b** $6x^2 \times 3x^4$
- **c** $5a^2b \times 4ab^3$
- **d** $4a^3b^4 - 2a^2b^3$

e $5a^4b^5 - 3a^4b^5$

f $\dfrac{4c^3 \times 7c^5}{2c^2 \times c^3}$

g $\dfrac{\left(8y^6\right)^2 \times 3y}{12y^3}$

h $\dfrac{4p^3q^2 \times 3p^4q^3}{6p^5q^4}$

i $\dfrac{3pq \times 16p^3q^2}{12p^7q^3}$

j $\dfrac{16p^4}{(2p^2)^3}$

k $\dfrac{\left(2m^2n^3\right) \times \left(3m^3n^2\right)}{4m^4n^4}$

l $4p^2q^3 \times 3p^3q^3 \div (3p^2q^2)^2$

m $\dfrac{10p^8}{5p^{-5}}$

n $10a^2b^3 \times 4a^3b^2 - 4a^5b^5$

o $\dfrac{2b^2 \times 3b^3 \times 4b^4 \times 5b^5}{10b^{10}}$

7 Simplify.
- **a** $x^5 \times x^3 \times x^4$
- **b** $\sqrt{(x^3)^4}$
- **c** $\dfrac{x^2 \times x^{\frac{1}{2}}}{4\sqrt{x}}$
- **d** $4\sqrt{n^3}$
- **e** $m^6n^2 \div m^5n$
- **f** $4\sqrt{81k^8}$
- **g** $\dfrac{p^6 \times p^{-4}}{p^5}$
- **h** $(49t^2)^{\frac{1}{2}}$
- **i** $(3p^{-2})^2$
- **j** $\sqrt{36m^6n^4}$

8 Write each of these as a power of 2.
- **a** 64
- **b** $16^{\frac{3}{4}}$
- **c** 0.125
- **d** 1
- **e** $2^3 \times \sqrt{2}$
- **f** $2^n \times 2^{n+1}$

9 Write this expression as a power of a single base.

$$\frac{8^{3a} \times 4^b}{2^3 \times 16^{2b}}$$

10 If $5^x = 8$ and $5^y = 6$ find the value of

a 5^{x+y} b $(5^x)^2$
c 5^{3y} d 5^{x-y}
e 25^y f 125^x

Exercise B

In 1 to 5, work out the exact value without a calculator.

1 a 5^{-1} b 5^0
  c $25^{\frac{1}{2}}$ d $125^{\frac{2}{3}}$
  e $8^{\frac{5}{3}}$ f $16^{-0.25}$

2 a $27^{\frac{5}{3}}$ b $1000^{\frac{2}{3}}$
  c $32^{\frac{4}{5}}$ d 8^{-2}
  e $4^{\frac{5}{2}}$ f $0.01^{-1.5}$

3 a $36^{-\frac{1}{2}}$ b $6^{-2} \div 6^{-3}$
  c $64^{\frac{5}{6}}$ d $9^{\frac{1}{2}}$
  e $(25^2)^{-\frac{1}{2}}$ f $\sqrt{1\frac{11}{25}}$

4 a $3^2 \times 16^{\frac{1}{2}}$
  b $3^{-1} \times 5^{-2}$

c $2^{-2} + 6^0 + 5^{-1}$

d $64^{\frac{2}{3}} \times 8^{\frac{-1}{3}}$

e $4^3 - 81^{\frac{1}{4}} + \left(\frac{1}{8}\right)^{\frac{1}{3}}$

5 Evaluate.

a $\dfrac{36^2 \times \left(6^3\right)^2}{\sqrt{36} \times 6^4}$ b $9^{\frac{3}{2}} \div 3^2 \times \sqrt[3]{27^2}$

6 What is half of 4^6? Give your answer in index notation.

7 Find the missing index.

a $\dfrac{1}{\sqrt{10}} = 10^{\square}$

b $\sqrt[3]{6^2} = 6^{\square}$

c $8^{-3} \div 2 = 2^{\square}$

Exercise C

Find the value of x in each of these equations.

1 $3^x = 81$

2 $2^{x+2} = 64$

3 $4^{-x} = \dfrac{1}{16}$

4 $5^{2x} = 625$

5 $10^{2x} = 0.01$

6 $3^{-2x} = 27$

7 $\dfrac{1}{6^x} = \sqrt{36^2}$

8 $5^{x+3} = 25^2$

9 $81^x = 9^4$

10 $100^{3x} = 10 \times \dfrac{1}{100}$

11 $3^3 \times 9^{4x} = 3^2$

12 $4^{3x} = \dfrac{1}{\sqrt{2^8}}$

13 $\sqrt{100} = 10^{-x}$

14 $\left(\dfrac{1}{3}\right)^{2x} = 81^{-2}$

15 $5^3 \times 25^{2x} = (\sqrt[4]{125})^6$

This chapter is about

- expanding a single bracket
- expanding and simplifying an expression with brackets
- multiplying two sets of brackets
- squaring brackets
- solving problems involving brackets (including proof of identities).

Exercise A

Expand these brackets.

1 $7(3a + 6b)$

2 $-5(2c + 3d)$

3 $-4(3e + 5f)$

4 $3(7g - 2h)$

5 $3(4i + 2j - 3k)$

6 $-3(5m - 2n + 3p)$

7 $6(4r - 3s - 2t)$

8 $8(4r + 2s + t)$

9 $4(3u + 5v)$

10 $-6(4w + 3x)$

11 $2(5y + z)$

12 $4(3y + 2z)$

13 $-5(3v + 2)$

14 $3(7 + 4w)$

15 $-5(1 - 3a)$

16 $3(8g - 5)$

17 $x(2x + y)$

18 $5p(2p - 1)$

19 $ab(a - b^2)$

20 $-2k(5 - 3k)$

In 21 to 28 expand and simplify.

21 $4 + 3(2a - 1) - 4a$

22 $3(2p + 1) - (p + 7)$

23 $x + 2(3x - 1) - 5$

24 $5t(2t - 1) - t(6t + 5)$

25 $8 - (3y + 5) + 2(6 - y)$

26 $x(3x + 4) + 2x(x - 1)$

27 $4b - 2(3b + 4) + 5 - b$

28 $5t + 3(r - 2) - 6t + r$

29 Find the area of this shape in terms of x. All the lengths are in cm.

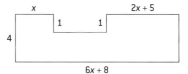

30

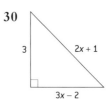

All the lengths are in cm.
Find the expression in terms of x for
  i   the perimeter
  ii   the area

Exercise B

In 1 to 30 expand the brackets.

1 $(x + 1)(x + 2)$

2 $(x + 3)(x + 4)$

3 $(x + 2)(x - 1)$

4 $(x + 5)(x - 3)$

5 $(x - 1)(x - 2)$

6 $(x + 1)(x - 5)$

7 $(x + 3)(x - 3)$

8 $(x + 2)^2$

9 $(x - 7)^2$

10 $(x - 12)(x - 9)$

11 $(x - 4)(x - 5)$

12 $(x + 3)(x - 7)$

13 $(x - 8)(4x - 1)$

14 $(2x + 4)(3x + 2)$

15 $(3x + 5)(x - 2)$

16 $(4x + 3)(2x - 4)$

17 $(7x - 2)(2x - 7)$

18 $(3x - 5)(2x + 3)$

19 $(3x + 7)^2$

20 $(3a + 4b)(5a + 2b)$

21 $(2m - 3n)(3m + 2n)$

22 $(5p - 3q)(2p - q)$

23 $(a + 3b)(3a - 2b)$

24 $(3x - 4y)(2x + 3y)$

25 $(5a + 2b)(5a - 2b)$

26 $(a + b)(a - 2b)$

27 $3(2p - 1)(3p + 4)$

28 $(x - 2)^2 + (x + 2)^2$

29 $(3y - 1)^3$

30 $10 - (2x + 3)^2$

31 Find an expression for the area of this trapezium.
Simplify your answer.
All the lengths are in centimetres.

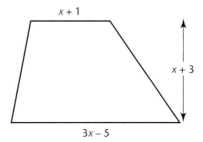

32 Find the values of a and b for which
$p^2 - 8p + a \equiv (p + b)^2$.

33 Prove that $(2x + 1)^2 - 3x - (x + 1)$ is always a multiple of 4.

34 Prove that $(2x + 1)^2 - 3x^2 - (1 - x) \equiv x(x + 5)$.

35 Find the value of c for which
$(x + c)^2 \equiv x^2 + 12x + c^2$

36 Find d given that
$(x + d)^2 \equiv x^2 + 2dx + 16$

CHAPTER 17 Linear equations

This chapter is about
- solving a basic linear equation
- solving an equation with variables on both sides
- solving an equation with brackets
- solving an equation with fractions
- solving a variety of problems by forming and solving a suitable equation.

Exercise A

Solve these equations.

1 $2x + 5 = 19$

2 $3x - 2 = 16$

3 $11 = 3x + 5$

4 $2 - 5x = 6$

5 $4x + 7 = 13$

6 $4x + 9 = 1$

7 $11 - 2x = 1$

8 $-6 - 4x = 3$

9 $40 = 25 - 2p$

10 $6y - 2 = 13$

11 $8a - 3 = -5$

12 $0 = 1 - 2k$

13 $4 - 3y = -2$

14 $4 = 10 + 2d$

15 $12x - 1 = 29$

16 $5 - 4x = -2$

Exercise B

Solve these equations.

1 $5x - 1 = 3x + 5$

2 $5x + 1 = 2x + 13$

3 $7x - 2 = 2x + 8$

4 $6x + 1 = 4x + 21$

5 $9x - 10 = 4x + 5$

6 $5x - 8 = 3x - 6$

7 $6x + 2 = 10 - 2x$

8 $2x - 10 = 5 - 3x$

9 $15 + 3x = 2x + 18$

10 $2x - 5 = 4 - x$

11 $3x - 2 = x + 7$

12 $x - 1 = 2x - 6$

13 $2x - 4 = 2 - x$

14 $9 - x = x + 5$

15 $3x - 2 = x - 8$

16 $6y = 5 - 2y + 3$

17 $4p - 3 = 9p - 2$

18 $3a + 6 + 5a = 9 - 2a + 4$

19 $3t - 1 + t = -5 + 4t - t$

20 $8 - 6y + 3 = 2y - 1$

Exercise C

Solve these equations.

1 $3(x - 2) = 18$

2 $4 + 2(1 + x) = 8$

3 $3(x - 5) = 6$

4 $10 - 2(x + 3) = 4$

5 $5(2x - 3) = 15$

6 $3 + 2(8 - 3y) = 5y + 1$

7 $4 - 3(2a + 3) - 5 = 2a - 1$

8 $2 - 3(t + 2) + 4(t - 3) = 9t$

9 $6(3p - 2) - 4 = 1 - 2(3p + 1)$

10 $4 - (h + 6) = 5h - 2(3 - h)$

11 $2(x - 3) + 3x = 6(x - 2)$

12 $3(x + 2) + 2(x - 5) - 4(x - 6) = 25$

13 $4(3y + 2) - 3(2y + 1) = 7$

14 $3(x + 2) - 2(x + 1) + 5(x - 2) = 15$

15 $4(x - 1) - (3x + 2) = 2(x + 7)$

16 $3 - 2(2x - 5) + 3(2 - x) = 1 - x$

Exercise D

Solve these equations.

1 $\dfrac{x}{2} = 5x - 18$

2 $\dfrac{2x}{5} = x - 12$

3 $\dfrac{2x}{3} = 10 - x$

4 $\dfrac{3x}{2} = 5x - 1$

5 $\dfrac{x}{5} + 4 = 11$

6 $\dfrac{40}{x} = 5$

7 $\dfrac{300}{x} = 6$

8 $\dfrac{20}{3x} = 2$

9 $\dfrac{1}{5}(3x - 2) = 5$

10 $\dfrac{3x - 10}{4} = 2x$

11 $\dfrac{12}{x} + 5 = 13$

12 $\dfrac{7}{3x} - 4 = 1$

13 $\dfrac{x}{3} - \dfrac{x}{5} = 2$

14 $\dfrac{2x}{3} - \dfrac{x}{4} = 5$

15 $\dfrac{2x - 1}{3} = \dfrac{x + 5}{2}$

16 $\dfrac{5 + x}{x - 3} = 2$

Exercise E

Solve these equations.

1 $\dfrac{x}{3} + \dfrac{2x}{5} = 1$

2 $\dfrac{x}{7} + \dfrac{1}{3} - \dfrac{2}{7} = -\dfrac{2}{3}$

3 $\dfrac{x + 1}{4} + \dfrac{x - 1}{3} = \dfrac{17}{12}$

4 $\dfrac{2(x - 1)}{5} + \dfrac{3(1 - x)}{2} = \dfrac{19}{10}$

5 $\dfrac{x}{3} - \dfrac{x - 1}{4} = 7$

6 $\dfrac{x + 1}{5} + \dfrac{x - 3}{3} = 4$

7 $\dfrac{2(x-4)}{3} - \dfrac{x+2}{5} - 3 = 0$

8 $\dfrac{3x-1}{2} - \dfrac{x-2}{5} = 9$

9 $\dfrac{1}{2}(x+3) - \dfrac{1}{3}(x+2) = 4$

10 $\dfrac{2}{3}(x+1) + \dfrac{3}{4}(x-2) = 1$

11 $\dfrac{x+4}{3} + \dfrac{2x+3}{2} - 2 = 0$

12 $\dfrac{1}{6}(2x+5) - \dfrac{1}{4}(x-3) = \dfrac{2}{3}(8-4x) + 1$

Exercise F

1 A triangle has a base of b cm and a perpendicular height of 7 cm. The area is $21\,\text{cm}^2$. Write down an equation in b and solve it to find the length of the base.

2 Emma thinks of a number. Her number divided by 3 gives the same answer as dividing her number by 4 and adding 2. Let the number be n. Write down an equation in n and solve it to find the number Emma thought of.

3 James had a rope x metres long. He cut off 7 metres and there was still three quarters of the rope left.
   a Write down an equation in x.
   b Solve your equation to find how much rope James started with.

4 Grace had £80. She bought a pair of jeans for £x. The amount she has left is one third of what she has spent.
   a Write down an equation in x.   **b** Solve the equation to find the amount spent.

5 The angles of a triangle are as shown in the diagram.

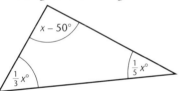

   a Write down an equation in x.
   b Solve the equation to find the angles of the triangle.

6 The lengths of the sides in this quadrilateral are in centimetres. The perimeter of the quadrilateral is 68 cm.

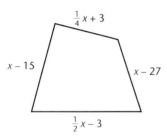

   a Write down an equation in x.
   b Solve the equation to find the lengths of the sides in this quadrilateral.

7 Three consecutive odd numbers have a sum of 381. What are the three numbers?

8 Finn buys 8 packets of crisps at 42 pence each and k ice lollies at 24 pence each. He pays with a £5 note and gets 44 pence change. Write an equation in k and solve it to find how many ice lollies he buys.

9 Calculate the perimeter of the equilateral triangle.

CHAPTER 18

Sequences

> ## This chapter is about
>
> - recognising special number sequences
> - describing the pattern for a sequence in words
> - continuing a sequence (including use of the difference method)
> - writing a sequence from given information
> - finding the nth term of a linear sequence
> - finding the nth term of a quadratic sequence
> - solving a variety of problems using sequences
> - recognising the role of counterexamples in the context of sequences.

1 Write down the next three terms in each of these sequences.

   a 7, 10, 13, 16, …, …, …   **b** 87, 80, 73, 66, …, …, …
   c 0.2, 0.4, 0.6, 0.8, …, …, …   **d** 1, 8, 15, 22, 29, 36, …, …, …
   e 7, 8, 10, 13, 17, …, …, …   **f** 9, 17, 25, 33, 41, 49, …, …, …
   g 4, 3, 5, 2, 6, …, …, …   **h** 16, 21, 26, 31, 36, 41, …, …, …
   i 20, 18, 14, 8, …, …, …   **j** 100, 50, 25, 12.5, …, …, …

2 Write down the first four terms of each of these sequences.

   a Starts with 3 and 3 is added each time.
   b Starts with 26 and 2 is subtracted each time.
   c Starts with 1 and it is multiplied by 10 each time.
   d Starts with x and 4 is added each time.
   e Starts with 1000 and it is divided by 10 each time.
   f Starts with n and it is halved each time.

3 Write down a rule in words which generates each of these sequences and hence write down the next three terms.

   a 24, 12, 6, 3, …,   **b** 100, 99, 98, 97, …,
   c 1, 2, 4, 8, …,   **d** 6, 5.5, 5, 4.5, …,
   e 29, 23, 17, 11, …,   **f** 25, 18, 11, 4, …,
   g 16, 11, 6, 1, …,   **h** 2, 4, 8, 16, 32, …,
   i 27, 19, 11, 3, …,   **j** 42, 29, 16, 3, …,
   k 1, 1, 2, 3, 5, …,   **l** 22, 17, 12, 7, …,

4 Find the missing numbers in each of these sequences. For each sequence, write down the term-to-term rule that connects the numbers.

   a 1, 7, …, 19, 25, …   **b** 11, …, 35, 47, …, 71   **c** 85, …, 67, …, 49, 40
   d …, 87, 83, 79, …, 71   **e** 7, 22, …, …, 67, 82   **f** 34, …, 20, 13, 6, …

5 Use the difference method to find the next 3 terms in each of these sequences.

   a 0, 1, 4, 9, 16, …, …, …   **b** −1, 4, 15, 32, 55, …, …, …   **c** 2, 9, 18, 29, 42, …, …, …

6 Find the rule for the nth term for each of these sequences.

a 2, 4, 6, 8, …
b 4, 7, 10, 14, …
c 0, 3, 6, 9, …
d 21, 22, 23, 24, …
e 1, 5, 9, 13, …
f 10, 13, 16, 19, …
g −3, −1, 1, 3, …
h 25, 20, 15, 10, …
i 4, 2, 0, −2, …
j 3, 2, 1, 0, …
k −3, −6, −9, −12, …
l $\frac{1}{6}, \frac{2}{7}, \frac{3}{8}, \frac{4}{9}, \dots$

7 Find the first four terms of each sequence given by the nth term.

a $n + 6$
b $6n$
c $n - 2$
d $3n + 2$
e $2n - 7$
f $3n - 2$
g $4n + 4$
h $-n$
i $5n + 2$
j $1 - 2n$
k $3 - n^2$
l $5 + 2n^2$

8 The 4th term of a sequence is 30, the 5th term is 39 and the 6th term is 48. Find the nth term of this sequence.

9 The 4th term of a sequence is 8, the 6th term is 14 and the 8th term is 20. Find the nth term of this sequence and hence find the 100th term.

10 Which term in the sequence 1, 7, 13, 19, … will be 79?

11 Here are four patterns made using sticks.

Pattern 1   Pattern 2   Pattern 3   Pattern 4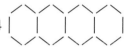

a How many sticks will be needed for pattern 10?
b Find a rule connecting the number of sticks (s) and the pattern number (p).
c How many sticks are needed for pattern 15?
d Which pattern number can be created with 81 sticks?

12 a Find a rule connecting n and T.

n	1	2	3	4
T	4	7	10	13

b Find a rule connecting r and K.

r	2	3	5	6
K	7	11	19	23

c Find a rule connecting m and P.

m	3	6	8	10
P	8	23	33	43

d Find a rule connecting d and W.

d	2	5	8	10
W	9	15	21	25

13 Here are three patterns of tiles.

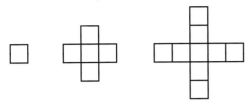

a Copy and complete this table

Pattern	1	2	3	4	5	n
Squares						

b Which pattern has 57 squares?

14 Here are three patterns of squares and crosses.

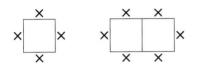

a Copy and complete this table

Squares	1	2	3	4	5	n
Crosses						

b How many crosses are needed for 18 squares?
c If there are 78 crosses, how many squares are there?
d Is it possible to have a pattern with 53 crosses? Explain your answer.

15 Prove that every term in this sequence is 6.

$(3 \times 4 - 1 \times 6), (4 \times 5 - 2 \times 7), (5 \times 6 - 3 \times 8), (6 \times 7 - 4 \times 9)$ …

16 How many terms of the sequence with nth term $12n - 3$ can be listed before a term greater than 180 occurs?

17 A sequence is given by nth term $\dfrac{4n - 3}{n^2}$

Two terms of the sequence are 1. Which two terms?

CHAPTER 19

Factorisation

This chapter is about

- factorising using common factors
- factorising using grouping
- factorising using the difference of two squares
- factorising quadratics
- simplifying expressions involving several types of factorisation.

Exercise A

Factorise these expressions fully.

1 $8x + 20$

2 $3x + 6$

3 $9x - 12$

4 $5x - 30$

5 $16 + 8x$

6 $9 + 15x$

7 $12 - 16x$

8 $8 - 12x$

9 $4x^2 + 16x$

10 $6x^2 + 30x$

11 $8x^2 - 20x$

12 $9x^2 - 15x$

13 $6x + 3y$

14 $4a - 10b$

15 $5a + 7a^2$

16 $6x^2 - 4x$

17 $3a^2 - ab + ac$

18 $4xy + 2y^2 - y$

19 $2y + 8xy$

20 $9a^2 + 3ab$

21 $8ab - 4ab^2$

22 $a^3 + a^2b$

23 $2x^2 - x^2y$

24 $6x^3 - 15xy$

25 $5a^2b + 15ab^2$

26 $12abc + 15ab^2 - 3a^2c$

27 $8x^2yz + 4xy^2z + 12xyz$

28 $2\pi rh + 2\pi r^2$

29 $3x^2 - x^4$

30 $6p^2q + 10pq^3 + 8pq^2$

Exercise B

Factorise each of these expressions.

1 $ak + bk + am + bm$

2 $p^3 + 3p^2 - 6 - 2p$

3 $ab - ac + bc^2 - c^3$

4 $x^2 + x - xz - z$

5 $6a^3 + 2a^2t - t^2 - 3at$

6 $m^2 - nt + mn - mt$

7 $r^3 + r^2 + r + 1$

8 $ac - 8 + a - 8c$

9 $6c^2 - cd - 48c + 8d$

10 $12ac - 2ab + 18cd - 3bd$

Exercise C

Factorise the expressions in 1 to 20.

1 $x^2 - 9$

2 $x^2 - 64$

3 $x^2 - 196$

4 $x^2 - y^2$

5 $25 - y^2$

6 $16 - c^2$

7 $a^2 - 10\,000$

8 $81 - s^2$

9 $x^2 - 36$

10 $49 - y^2$

11 $9x^2 - 25$

12 $4y^2 - 9$

13 $1 - 64t^2$

14 $x^2 - 121y^2$

15 $81a^2 - 16b^2$

16 $36a^2 - 25b^2$

17 $100 - 49y^2$

18 $2x^2 - 50y^2$

19 $p^2 - \dfrac{1}{100}$

20 $0.25a^2 - 0.36b^2$

21 Evaluate each of these without a calculator.
   a $59^2 - 58^2$
   b $(7\frac{1}{2})^2 - (6\frac{1}{2})^2$
   c $20001^2 - 19999^2$

22 Use the difference of two squares to simplify
   $$(4x + 3)^2 - (3x + 3)^2$$

Exercise D

Factorise these expressions.

1 $x^2 + 4x + 3$

2 $x^2 + 7x + 12$

3 $x^2 - 5x + 4$

4 $x^2 + 21x + 20$

5 $x^2 + 10x + 9$

6 $x^2 + 9x + 20$

7 $a^2 - 9a + 8$

8 $a^2 - 10a + 16$

9 $y^2 - 11y + 30$

10 $x^2 - 17x + 16$

11 $x^2 + 2x - 15$

12 $x^2 + 6x - 7$

13 $x^2 - 5x - 14$

14 $x^2 + 5x - 36$

15 $x^2 + 9x - 10$

16 $a^2 + 4a - 12$

17 $b^2 + 5b - 24$

18 $c^2 - 5c - 36$

19 $x^2 + 13x - 14$

20 $a^2 - 4a - 21$

21 $x^2 + 8x + 12$

22 $2x^2 - 5x + 2$

23 $4x^2 - 8x + 3$

24 $4x^2 + 21x + 5$

25 $5x^2 - 16x + 3$

26 $x^2 - x - 12$

27 $2x^2 - 5x - 12$

28 $6x^2 + x - 1$

29 $8x^2 - 2x - 3$

30 $6x^2 - 7x - 10$

Exercise E

Factorise fully each of these expressions.

1 $p^3 - p$

2 $4x^2 + 2x - 42$

3 $12x^2y^3 + 20xy^2$

4 $10b^2 - 10$

5 $3xy + 6x + 3y + 6$

6 $40 - 6k - 4k^2$

7 $6x^2 + 6xy + y^2$

8 $6c^2 - cd - d^2$

9 $8m^2 + 26mn + 15n^2$

10 $10w^2 + 19ew - 15e^2$

CHAPTER 20

Formulae

This chapter is about

- finding the value of a defined quantity using a formula
- changing the subject of a formula involving brackets, fractions, powers or roots
- changing the subject of a formula where the subject appears more than once
- solving problems requiring formulae and changing the subject.

Exercise A

1 For the formula $F = a^2 - b^2$, find F when $a = 1.2$, $b = 0.5$

2 For the formula $C = 5e^2 + 6f$, find C when $e = 1.5$, $f = 2.6$

3 A regular polygon has n sides. The size of each angle A can be found from the formula
$A = 180 - \dfrac{360}{n}$. Calculate the size of each angle A in

   a a regular nonagon.
                                    b a regular 20-sided polygon.

4 The formula for converting a temperature F degrees Fahrenheit to C degrees Celsius is
$C = \dfrac{5}{9}(F - 32)$.

   a Calculate C when F is 86.
                                b Calculate F when C is 120.

5 $T = 2\pi\sqrt{\dfrac{L}{g}}$. Find T when $L = 40$ and $g = 9.8$. Give your answer correct to 3 significant figures.

6 $v^2 = u^2 + 2as$. Calculate v when $u = 54$, $a = 9.8$ and $s = 0.6$.

7 The volume of a container V is given by $V = \dfrac{1}{3}\pi h(2R^2 - r^2)$ where r is the radius of the
base, R is the radius of the top and h is the height of the container. Calculate V when
$\pi = \dfrac{22}{7}$, $h = 14$, $R = \dfrac{2}{3}$ and $r = \dfrac{1}{2}$. Give your answer as a mixed number.

8 A man travels x km to work and then home again each day. On a particular day his mileometer
shows m miles. After p days his mileometer now shows k miles.

   a Assuming his only journeys are to and from work, write a formula for k in terms of x, p and m.
   b Hence calculate k when $x = 32$, $p = 12$ and $m = 82$.

Exercise B

1 Rearrange each formula to make the letter in brackets the subject.
   a $a + b + c = 180$ (b)
                                    b $x = 5y + c$ (y)
   c $c = p - 3t$ (t)
                                    d $p = 2g - 2f$ (g)

2 Make h the subject in $S = \pi r^2 + 2\pi rh$

3 Make a the subject in $v - at = u$

4 Make r the subject in $C = 2\pi r$

5 Make x the subject in $dx + e = f$

6 Make t the subject in $p - 3t - r = 5t + 1$

7 Rearrange each formula to make the letter in brackets the subject.

   a $A = \dfrac{bh}{2}$ (h) **b** $a = 180(n - 2)$ (n)

   c $A = p(q + r)$ (q) **d** $F = \dfrac{m + 4n}{t}$ (n)

8 Make x the subject in $4(x - y) = 8y + x$

9 Make x the subject in $y = \dfrac{8}{x} - 3$

10 Make m the subject in $E = \dfrac{1}{2}mv^2$

11 Make h the subject in $V = \dfrac{1}{3}\pi r^2 h$

12 Make R the subject in $T = \dfrac{PRT}{100}$

13 Rearrange each formula to make the letter in brackets the subject.

   a $A = 2\pi r^2 h$ (r) **b** $P = 1 + a^2$ (a)

   c $a^2 = b^2 + c^2$ (c) **d** $y = 3x^2 - 4$ (x)

14 Make v the subject in $v^2 - u^2 = 2as$

15 Make t the subject in $S = 15 - \dfrac{1}{2}at^2$

16 Make x the subject in $\sqrt{x} = tv$

17 Make x the subject in $p^2 + q^2 = (x + y)(x - y)$

18 Make v the subject in $r = \sqrt[3]{\dfrac{3v}{4\pi}}$

19 Rearrange each formula to make the letter in brackets the subject.

   a $f = \dfrac{uv}{u - v}$ (u) **b** $pq + r = rq - p$ (r)

   c $y = x + \dfrac{px}{q}$ (x) **d** $s = ut + \dfrac{at}{2}$ (t)

   e $pq - rs = rt$ (r) **f** $y = \dfrac{x + 4}{x - 3}$ (x)

   g $K = \dfrac{2y}{3 + y}$ (y) **h** $\dfrac{1}{uv} + \dfrac{1}{v} = \dfrac{1}{f^2}$ (v)

20 Decide if each of these is an expression, equation, formula or identity.

   a $2x + 3 = 1$ **b** $5x + 4 = 4 + 5x$ **c** $3x^2 + 8$

   d $d = 5x^2 - 7$ **e** $6x + 3 = 2x$ **f** $x(x + 4) = x^2 + 4x$

CHAPTER 21

Proportion and variation

This chapter is about

- solving numerical problems involving direct or inverse proportion
- solving problems involving direct or inverse variation, algebraically by setting up a formula involving the constant of proportionality
- using the formula derived for direct or inverse variation to find further unknown quantities
- recognising graphs which represent variables which are directly or inversely proportional.

1 Eight men build a wall in 20 days. How long would it take if there were 10 men?

2 Twelve pens cost £4.44. How much would 5 of these pens cost?

3 A recipe for 6 people uses 150 g of butter and 210 g of flour.
How much of each will be needed if the recipe is adapted for 10 people?

4 A car travelling at 80 km/h can complete a journey in 4 hours.
How long would it take to complete the same journey if the car was travelling at 60 km/h?

5 Five photocopiers print a total of 3800 pages in 20 minutes.
If one photocopier breaks down, how many pages will be printed in the next half hour?

6 A team of 24 factory workers produce x items per day.
If production is to be increased by 25%, how many workers will be needed?

7 y is directly proportional to w. $y = 20$ when $w = 5$.
  a Find a formula connecting y and w.
  b Find y when $w = 8$.
  c Find w when $y = 6$.

8 m is inversely proportional to h. $m = 2$ when $h = 8$.
  a Find a formula connecting m and h.
  b Find m when $h = 20$.
  c Find h when $m = 100$.

9 $y \propto x^2$ and $y = 13$ when $x = 2$. Find y when $x = 5$.

10 As part of their training, astronauts have to experience the effects of large accelerations, called 'G forces'. The training consists of being placed in a pod at the end of a rotor arm which is spun at speed. The force experienced, F, is proportional to the square of the speed, s, of the pod. This relationship can be written as $F \propto s^2$. When the pod is spinning with a speed of 6 m/s the force experienced is 2G. How many Gs will be experienced when the speed is 18 m/s?

11 y is proportional to the square root of x. When $x = 25$, $y = 15$. Calculate x when $y = 24$.

12 The weight of a spherical particle varies directly as the cube of its radius. A particle of radius 4 mm, weighs 115.2 g.
  a What is the weight of a particle of radius 8 mm?
  b A particle has weight 77.175 g. What is its radius?

13 Given that $t \propto r^3$, what is the effect on t when
  a r is doubled?
  b r is divided by 3?

14

r	2	3	6
P	1.6	3.6	14.4

Which law connects the values in the table?

$$p \propto r, \qquad p \propto r^2, \qquad p \propto r^3$$

15 Boyle's law states that the pressure of a gas, P pascals, varies inversely with its volume, $V \mathrm{m}^3$, at constant temperature.
  a If $P = 10$ pascals when $V = 100 \mathrm{m}^3$, find the formula connecting P and V.
  b Find P when $V = 500 \mathrm{m}^3$

16 $y \propto \dfrac{1}{x^2}$ and $y = 5$ when $x = 2$. Find y when $x = 5$.

17 The gravitational force, F, between a satellite and the Earth is inversely proportional to the square of its distance, d, from the centre of the Earth. The rule can be written as $F \propto \dfrac{1}{d^2}$.

  a The radius of the Earth is 6400 km. So, at 12 800 km above the Earth's surface, d is three times its value on the Earth's surface. What is the effect on the gravitational force at this height?
  b How far above the Earth's surface is the satellite when the gravitational force is one quarter that on the Earth's surface?

18 Given that $p \propto \dfrac{1}{\sqrt{r}}$, copy and complete the table of values.

r	100	4	
p	1.2		3

19 The intensity of the illumination from a light bulb is inversely proportional to the square of the distance from the bulb. What needs to happen to the distance for the illumination to be four times greater?

20 The temperature t (°C) of sea water is inversely proportional to the depth below sea level d (m). At a depth of 400 m the temperature was 6 °C. How far below sea level will the temperature be 1.5 °C?

CHAPTER 22

Trial and improvement

This chapter is about

- solving a polynomial equation by trial and improvement, correct to 1 decimal place
- solving a polynomial equation by trial and improvement, correct to 2 decimal places
- solving a problem, in context, by trial and improvement, to a suitable degree of accuracy.

1 Show that a solution of $x^3 - 2x - 1 = 0$ lies between 1 and 2.
Use trial and improvement to find the solution correct to 1 decimal place.

2 Show that a solution of $x^3 + 5x - 3 = 0$ lies between 0 and 1.
Use trial and improvement to find the solution correct to 1 decimal place.

3 Show that a solution of $x^3 - 5x + 2 = 0$ lies between -3 and -2.
Use trial and improvement to find the solution correct to 1 decimal place.

4 Show that the equation $x^3 - 5x + 2 = 0$ has another solution between 0 and 1.
Use trial and improvement to find this solution correct to 1 decimal place.

5 Show that the equation $\frac{2}{x} = x^2 - 2$ has a solution between $x = 1$ and $x = 2$.
Then find this solution, correct to 2 decimal places.

6 Solve the equation $x^3 - 2x = 180$ by trial and improvement.
Give your solution correct to 1 decimal place.

7 Solve the equation $4x^2 - 2x + 1 = 85$ by trial and improvement.
Give your solution correct to 1 decimal place.

8 Solve the equation $x^3 = 2x^2 + 5$ by trial and improvement.
Give your solution correct to 2 decimal places.

9 The cube of a number, subtracted from eight times the original number squared is 35.
Find the original number, correct to 1 decimal place.

10 The hypotenuse of a right-angled triangle is 25 m.
The base of the triangle is 4 m less than the height.
Calculate the height of the triangle correct to 1 decimal place.

11 The distance (s) metres travelled by a particle in t seconds is given by $s = 20t + 5t^2$.
Find the time taken by the particle to travel a distance of 120 m.
Give your answer correct to 2 decimal places.

CHAPTER 23

Algebraic fractions

This chapter is about

- simplifying an algebraic fraction, using factorisation and the rules of indices
- adding and subtracting algebraic fractions
- multiplying and dividing algebraic fractions

1 Simplify each of these fractions.

a $\dfrac{16}{20}$

b $\dfrac{24}{56}$

c $\dfrac{27}{45}$

2 Simplify each of these fractions.

a $\dfrac{4p^2q}{12p}$

b $\dfrac{36y}{(6y)^2}$

c $\dfrac{24pq^2}{40p^2q}$

3 Simplify each of these.

a $\dfrac{5(x+10)}{x(x+10)}$

b $\dfrac{3x(x-1)}{12(x-1)}$

c $\dfrac{5x(x+2)}{10x^2(x+2)}$

d $\dfrac{24x^2(x-3)}{30x^3(x-3)}$

4 Simplify each of these.

a $\dfrac{p^2-p}{p}$

b $\dfrac{18x^2y^3}{6x^2y-12xy^2}$

c $\dfrac{2a-1}{6a^2-3a}$

d $\dfrac{8-4t}{6-3t}$

e $\dfrac{x^2-2x}{x^2+x-6}$

f $\dfrac{t^2-1}{t+1}$

5 Simplify each of these.

a $\dfrac{7x}{x^2-5x}$

b $\dfrac{2x^2-6x}{x^2-x-6}$

c $\dfrac{x^2+2x-3}{x^2+8x+15}$

d $\dfrac{x^2+2x-8}{x^3-2x^2}$

e $\dfrac{x^2-7x+12}{x^2-9}$

f $\dfrac{x^2-5x}{2x^2-11x+5}$

g $\dfrac{3x^2+14x-5}{x^2+7x+10}$

h $\dfrac{9x^2-4}{3x^2-x-2}$

i $\dfrac{x^2-ax+bx-ab}{x^2-a^2}$

j $\dfrac{k^2-9r^2}{k^2-9kr+18r^2}$

6 Simplify each of these.

a $\dfrac{a}{2} + \dfrac{a+1}{3}$

b $\dfrac{2x-1}{5} + \dfrac{x+3}{2}$

c $\dfrac{x-3}{3} + \dfrac{x-2}{5}$

d $\dfrac{1}{b} + \dfrac{2}{b+1}$

e $\dfrac{5}{x-2} + \dfrac{3}{x+3}$

f $\dfrac{p-1}{3} + \dfrac{p+2}{4}$

g $\dfrac{p+1}{3} - \dfrac{2p+1}{4}$

h $\dfrac{2x+1}{7} - \dfrac{x+2}{3}$

i $\dfrac{3}{x-2} + \dfrac{4}{x}$

j $\dfrac{7}{m+1} - \dfrac{3}{m+2}$

k $\dfrac{x+1}{x+2} + \dfrac{x+2}{x+1}$

l $\dfrac{1}{x} - \dfrac{1}{x-1} + \dfrac{1}{x+1}$

m $\dfrac{5}{a^2+a} + \dfrac{2}{a^2-a}$

n $\dfrac{5p}{p^2-1} - \dfrac{2}{p+1}$

o $\dfrac{3}{2x-6} + \dfrac{2x}{x-3}$

7 Simplify each of these.

a $\dfrac{20a^2b^3}{5b} \times \dfrac{b^4}{2a}$

b $\dfrac{2x^2y-1}{6y^2} \times \dfrac{3y^2x}{2x^2}$

c $\dfrac{a-3}{15} \div \dfrac{2a-6}{5}$

d $\dfrac{4p^2}{9q} \div \dfrac{2p}{3q^2}$

e $\dfrac{m^2-q}{15} \times \dfrac{5}{m+q}$

f $\dfrac{4x-2}{15-3x} \div \dfrac{2x-1}{x-5}$

g $\dfrac{5+5t}{t-3} \times \dfrac{6-2t}{8t+8}$

h $\dfrac{k^2-t^2}{(k+t)^2} \times \dfrac{k+t}{k-t}$

i $\dfrac{a^2+5a+6}{a^2-5a+6} \div \dfrac{a^2+6a+8}{a^2-6a+8}$

j $\dfrac{10-2p}{p^2} \div \dfrac{p-5}{p}$

k $\left(\dfrac{3}{x+6} - \dfrac{2}{x}\right) \div \dfrac{4x-48}{x^2-36}$

l $\dfrac{16a^2b}{8a+4b} \times \dfrac{a}{2b} \div \dfrac{24a+12b}{(2a+b)^2}$

m $\dfrac{2x^2-18}{x^2+5x+6} \div \dfrac{x^2+2x-15}{2x^2+9x-5}$

CHAPTER 24

Solving quadratic equations

This chapter is about

- solving a quadratic equation by factorisation
- solving a quadratic equation using the quadratic formula
- solving algebraic fractional equations (including those with algebraic denominators)
- solving a variety of problems involving quadratic equations, by choosing an appropriate form of solution.

Exercise A

Solve these equations by factorisation.

1 **a** $x(x - 3) = 0$ **b** $(x - 2)(x + 6) = 0$ **c** $(4x + 1)^2 = 0$
   d $(2p - 1)(3p - 4) = 0$ **e** $2y(3y - 1) = 0$ **f** $5(2x - 1)(3x + 2) = 0$

2 **a** $x^2 + 4x + 3 = 0$ **b** $x^2 - x - 30 = 0$ **c** $3x^2 - 2x - 8 = 0$
   d $5x^2 - 23x + 12 = 0$ **e** $6x^2 + 19x - 20 = 0$ **f** $6x^2 + 7x - 5 = 0$

3 **a** $x^2 + 4x = 0$ **b** $x^2 - 49 = 0$ **c** $4y^2 - 36 = 0$
   d $6p^2 + p = 0$ **e** $h^2 - \dfrac{1}{36} = 0$ **f** $9x^2 - 25 = 0$

4 **a** $x^2 = 3x$ **b** $x^2 = 4x$ **c** $x^2 = 35 - 2x$
   d $3x^2 = 24x$ **e** $(x + 3)(x - 2) = 2(2x - 1)$ **f** $5x(x + 2) = 2x^2 - 3$

5 **a** $x^2 - 19x + 18 = 0$ **b** $3x^2 - 15x = 0$ **c** $4x^2 + 5x = 6$
   d $x(5x + 13) = 6$ **e** $\dfrac{p}{2} = 6p^2$ **f** $\dfrac{2m - 1}{3} = m(m + 2)$

6 Solve each of these equations, giving your answers correct to 2 decimal places.
   a $x^2 + 7x + 3 = 0$ **b** $5x^2 + 11x + 1 = 0$ **c** $3x^2 - x - 8 = 0$
   d $9x^2 + 6x - 19 = 0$ **e** $3x^2 + 8x - 9 = 0$ **f** $9x^2 - 8x + 1 = 0$

7 Solve each of these equations, giving the exact answers in surd form.
   a $x^2 + 4x - 10 = 0$ **b** $x^2 - 3x - 7 = 0$ **c** $x^2 + 18x - 35 = 0$
   d $9x^2 + 6x - 19 = 0$ **e** $2x^2 - 4x + 1 = 0$ **f** $5x^2 - 4x - 8 = 0$

8 Solve each of these equations, giving your answers correct to 3 significant figures.
   a $x^2 + 12x = 5$ **b** $\dfrac{x^2 + 2}{x} = 4$ **c** $(t - 3)^2 = 6$
   d $(x - 5)(x + 1) = 12$ **e** $x(x - 6) = -1$ **f** $x(1 - 3x) = 5x - 2$

Exercise B

Solve each of these equations. Give your answer either exact or correct to 2 decimal places.

1 $\dfrac{4}{x} + \dfrac{3}{2x} = \dfrac{11}{4}$

2 $x + 2 = \dfrac{x + 2}{x - 3}$

3 $\dfrac{2}{3x} - \dfrac{6}{5x} = -8$

4 $\dfrac{1}{x + 1} + \dfrac{1}{x - 1} = 4$

5 $(x - 2)(x + 5) = 6x + 8$

6 $\dfrac{2}{x - 1} - \dfrac{1}{x + 2} = \dfrac{1}{2}$

7 $\dfrac{3}{n - 2} - \dfrac{1}{2} = \dfrac{1}{n + 3}$

8 $\dfrac{6}{x} - 4 = \dfrac{-3}{x + 1}$

9 $\dfrac{10}{x - 1} + \dfrac{12}{x + 2} = \dfrac{7}{2}$

10 $\dfrac{5}{2p + 1} + \dfrac{4}{p + 1} = 3$

11 $(5 - 3x)(1 + 2x) = (x + 1)^2$

12 $\dfrac{5x}{x + 1} - \dfrac{3}{1 - 2x} + \dfrac{10}{3} = 0$

Exercise C

Solve each of these problems by forming and solving a suitable quadratic equation.

1 The length of a rectangle is 6 m greater than its width. The area of the rectangle is 160 m². Find the width.

2 The sum of the squares of two consecutive odd numbers is 650. Find the numbers.

3 The width of a rectangle is 7 cm less than its length. The diagonal is 1 cm more than the length. Calculate the length of the rectangle.

4 A driver has a journey of 300 km to complete. On one particular journey she travelled 10 km/h faster than her usual average speed and her journey took 1 hour less. What is her usual average speed?

5 Ellie has £3.20 to spend on pens. However, each pen is 2p dearer than she expected, so she has to buy 8 fewer than planned. What is the cost of each pen?

6 A 400 g packet of biscuits contains b biscuits. A 450 g packet has 5 extra biscuits, but each biscuit in the second packet is 1 g lighter than those in the first. Find the number of biscuits in the 400 g packet.

7

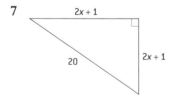

Calculate the perimeter of the triangle, correct to 2 decimal places. All the lengths are given in cm.

8 The sum of a number and its own reciprocal is 3.5125. Find the number and its reciprocal.

CHAPTER 25

Straight lines and linear graphs

This chapter is about

- recognising and drawing a linear graph
- finding the length of a line joining two points
- finding the midpoint of a line joining two points
- finding the gradient of a line
- knowing the properties of gradients, including the gradients of parallel and perpendicular lines
- understanding and using the equation $y = mx + c$
- drawing a straight line using the gradient and crossing point (including lines not given in the form $y = mx + c$)
- finding the equation of a straight line given the graph
- finding the equation of a straight line given the gradient and one point on the line
- finding the equation of a straight line given two points on the line.

Exercise A

1 **a** Copy and complete this table for the equation $y = 6x + 1$.

x	−3	−2	−1	0	1	2	3
$y = 6x + 1$		−11					

   b Draw the graph.

2 **a** Copy and complete this table for the equation $y = 3x - 5$.

x	−2	−1	0	1	2	3	4
$y = 3x - 5$							

   b Draw the graph.

3 **a** Copy and complete this table for the equation $y = 4 - 5x$.

x	−3	−2	−1	0	1	2	3
$y = 4 - 5x$							

   b Draw the graph.

4 **a** Copy and complete this table for the equation $y = 3x - 3$.

x	−2	0	4
$y = 3x - 3$			

   b Draw the graph of the equation $y = 3x - 3$ for values of x from −2 to 4.
   c From the graph find the value of x when $y = 4$.
       Give your answer correct to 1 decimal place.

5 Draw the graph of $3x + 4y = 12$.

6 Draw the graph of $2y - 5x = 15$.

7 a Does the point (2, 5) lie on the line $y = 2x + 3$?
  b Does the point (3, 1) lie on the line $y = 2x - 5$?
  c Does the point (−7, 0) lie on the line $y = 7 - x$?
  d Does the point (4, −2) lie on the line $2x - y = 10$?

8 (−2, k) lies on the line $3x + 2y = 4$. Find k.

9 For each of the lines in the diagram, find the coordinates of the midpoint.

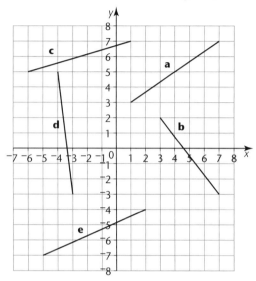

10 Find the coordinates of the midpoint of the line joining each of these pairs of points.

  a A(3, 7) and B(−5, 7)   **b** C(2, 1) and D(8, 5)
  c E(3, 7) and F(8, 2)   **d** G(1, 6) and H(9, 3)
  e I(−7, 1) and J(3, 6)   **f** K(−5, −6) and L(−7, −3)

11 B is the point (5, −3). The midpoint of AB is (1, 2). Find the coordinates of A.

12 Find the length of each of the lines in the diagram.
  When the answer is not exact, give your answer correct to 2 decimal places.

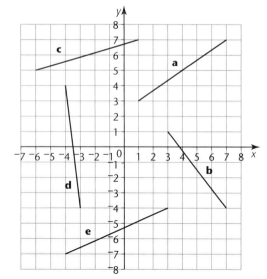

13 Find the length of the line joining each of these pairs of points.
When the answer is not exact, give your answer correct to 2 decimal places.
   a A(2, 2) and B(4, 7)   **b** C(2, 9) and D(7, 2)
   c E(−2, −4) and F(−3, 5)   **d** G(6, 3) and H(3, −1)
   e I(0, −6) and J(−5, 6)   **f** K(5, −7) and L(−3, 10)

14 A is (1, 3). B is (2, 5). C is (5, 1).
By finding the lengths of the three sides, show that triangle ABC is a right-angled triangle.

Exercise B

1 Find the gradient of each line.

a
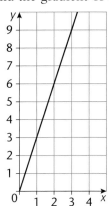

b
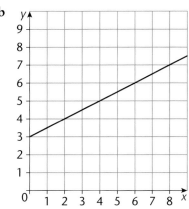

c
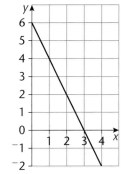

d
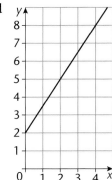

e
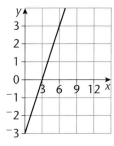

2 Work out the gradient of the line joining each of these pairs of points.
   a (1, 5) and (2, 8)   **b** (3, 4) and (5, 8)
   c (−1, 4) and (9, 6)   **d** (−2, 1) and (0, −7)
   e (−3, −4) and (−7, −3)   **f** (2, 1) and (−1, $\frac{1}{2}$)

3 Write down the gradient of each line.
   a $y = 7x + 2$ **b** $y = 5 − 4x$
   c $y = x + 8$ **d** $y = 4 − x$
   e $2y = 4x + 8$ **f** $3y + 12x = 5$
   g $7x − 2y = 3$ **h** $x + 3y = 6$

4 For each of these, which two lines are parallel?
    a $y = 2x + 4$ $y = 4x + 3$ $y = 4x + 5$
    b $y = 3x - 2$ $y = 5 + 3x$ $y = 5x - 5$
    c $y = 6 - x$ $y = 6 + 3x$ $y = -x + 3$
    d $y = x + 4$ $y = 2x + 1$ $2y = 2x + 3$
    e $3x + y = 2$ $y = 5 - 3x$ $y = 3x - 2$

5 Write down the gradient of a line which is parallel to $y = 6 - 4x$.

6 Write down the gradient of a line which is perpendicular to $y = 2x + 7$.

7 Write down the gradient of a line which is perpendicular to $y + 4x = 8$.

8 Write down the y-intercept of each of these lines.
    a $y = 3x + 5$ **b** $y = 6 - 2x$ **c** $y = 8x$
    d $2y = 3x + 4$ **e** $3y - x + 6 = 0$ **f** $8y - x + 2 = 0$

9 For each pair of lines, write down which line is steeper.
    a $y = 5x + 1$ $y = 2x + 7$ **b** $y = 3x - 8$ $y = x + 3$
    c $y = \dfrac{1}{2}x + 4$ $y = x + 2$ **d** $y = 5 + 6x$ $y = 10x + 4$

10 Match each line to its equation.

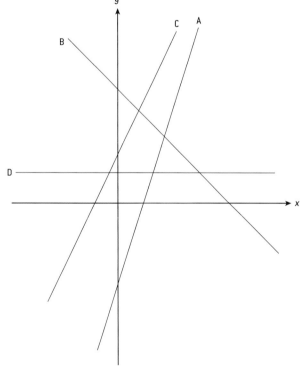

    i $y = 2x + 3$ **ii** $y = 2$ **iii** $y = 3x - 5$ **iv** $y = 7 - x$

11 Find the equation of the line with gradient 3 which passes through the point $(0, 7)$.

12 Find the equation of the line with gradient 2 which passes through the point $(0, -4)$.

13 Find the equation of each line.

a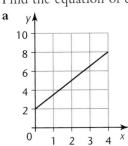

b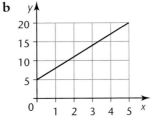

c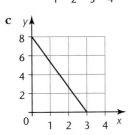

d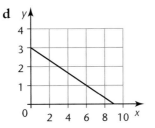

14 Find the equation of the line parallel to $y = 4x + 5$ which passes through $(0, 1)$.

15 Find the equation of the line parallel to $2y = 6x - 3$ which passes through $(0, -5)$.

16 Find the equation of the straight lines which pass through these pairs of points.

   a $(0, 2)$ and $(1, 6)$ **b** $(0, -4)$ and $(2, 4)$
   c $(0, 5)$ and $(3, -4)$ **d** $(3, 5)$ and $(4, 7)$
   e $(2, 5)$ and $(6, -3)$ **f** $(-2, -7)$ and $(3, -3)$

17 Find the equation of the straight line which passes through $(0, 10)$ and is perpendicular to $y = 4x + 3$.

18 Find the equation of the straight line which passes through $(-1, 5)$ and is parallel to $y - 3x = 4$

19 Find the equation of the straight line which passes through $(5, 4)$ and is perpendicular to $2y + 5x = 3$

20 A straight line has x intercept 3 and y intercept 6. Write down its equation.

CHAPTER 26

Non-linear graphs

This chapter is about

- recognising and drawing quadratic and cubic graphs
- recognising and drawing a reciprocal graph
- recognising and drawing an exponential graph
- recognising and drawing graphs of the trig functions sin, cos and tan.

Exercise A

1 Copy and complete this table for $y = x^2 + 3x - 5$. Draw the graph.

x	-2	-1	0	1	2	3	4	5
x^2								
$+3x$								
-5								
$y = x^2 + 3x - 5$								

2 Draw the graph of $y = 2 + x - x^2$, for values of x from -3 to 3.

3 Draw the graph of $y = 2x^2 - 3x - 1$, for values of x from -2 to 3.

4 Draw the graph of $y = (3 - 2x)(1 - x)$, for values of x from -2 to 4.

5 a Copy and complete the table for $y = x^3 - 5x$

x	-3	-2	-1	0	1	2	3
x^3	-27						
$-5x$	15						
y	-12						

   b Draw the graph of $y = x^3 - 5x$.

6 a Make a table of values for $y = x^3 + 4x^2 - 6$ for values of x from -4 to 2.
   b Draw the graph of $y = x^3 + 4x^2 - 6$.

7 Draw the graph of $y = x^3 + 3x^2$ for values of x from -3 to 2.

8 Draw the graph of $y = 5x - x^3$ for values of x from -3 to 3.

Exercise B

1 Draw the graph of $y = \dfrac{3}{x}$ for $-3 \leqslant x \leqslant 3$.

2 Draw the graph of $y = \dfrac{-10}{x}$ for $-5 \leqslant x \leqslant 5$.

3 Draw the graph of $y = \dfrac{1}{2x}$ for $-4 \leqslant x \leqslant 4$

4 Draw the graph of $y = \dfrac{8}{2-x}$.

Write down the equation of the vertical asymptote.

5 a Draw the graph of $y = 2.5^x$ for values of x from -2 to 4
 b Use your graph to estimate
  i the value of y when $x = 3.4$
  ii the value of x when $y = 11$

6 a Copy and complete this table of values for the equation $y = 0.8^x$

x	−8	−6	−4	−2	0	2	4	6	8
y	5.96			1.56	1				0.17

 b Draw the graph of $y = 0.8^x$ for values of x from -8 to 8.
 c Use your graph to solve these equations.
  i $0.8^x = 0.5$
  ii $0.8^x = 5$

7 Draw the graph of $y = 3^{-x}$ for values of x from -3 to 3.

8 Draw the graph of $y = 2^x + 1$ for values of x from -3 to 3. Write down the equation of the horizontal asymptote of this graph.

Exercise C

1 a Sketch the graph of $y = \cos x$ for values of x from $0°$ to $360°$.
 b Use your graph and your calculator to find the solutions of $\cos x = 0.5$ between $0°$ and $360°$.

2 a Sketch the graph of $y = \sin x$ for values of x from $0°$ to $360°$.
 b Use your graph and your calculator to find the solutions of $\sin x = 0.7071$ between $0°$ and $360°$.

3 Given that $\cos 40° = 0.766$, use the symmetry of the graph of $y = \cos x$ to find the solutions of $\cos x = -0.766$ between $0°$ and $360°$.

4 Give one other angle that has a sine value equal to each of these. Use the graph of $y = \sin x$.
 a $\sin 30°$ b $\sin 120°$ c $\sin 45°$ d $\sin 200°$

5 Give one other angle that has a cosine value equal to each of these. Use the graph of $y = \cos x$.
 a $\cos 120°$ b $\cos 30°$ c $\cos 210°$ d $\cos 90°$

6 For $0° \leqslant x \leqslant 360°$, solve these equations. Use the graphs and your calculator.
 a $\sin x = 0.1$ b $2 \cos x = 1$ c $\tan x = -3$ d $2 \sin x = \sqrt{3}$
 e $\cos x = -\sin x$

CHAPTER 27

Real-life graphs

This chapter is about

- using graphs to represent real-life functions
- understanding and using the terms exponential growth, exponential decay and half-life.

1   This graph shows what a plumber charges for his labour.
    The charge is made up of a call out fee and a cost per hour.

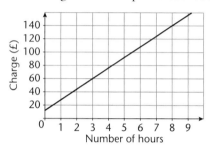

   a   What is the plumber's charge for 3 hours?
   b   What is the call out fee?
   c   What is the cost per hour?

2   This graph shows Michael's journey from Dorton to Canburn on a bicycle.

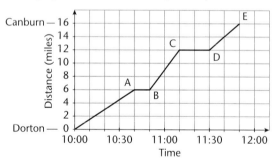

   a   Which parts of the graph show Michael not moving?
   b   At what time did Michael get to Canburn?
   c   How far did he travel altogether?
   d   Which part of the journey was Michael cycling fastest?
   e   Calculate Michael's average speed from D to E.

3 John and Imran live in the same block of flats and go to the same school. The graph represents their journeys home from school.

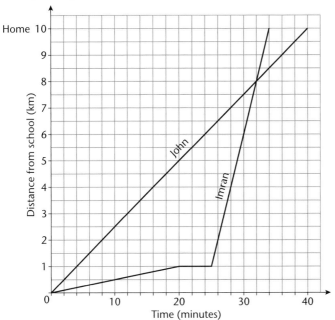

a Describe Imran's journey home.
b After how many minutes did Imran overtake John?
c How many minutes before John did Imran arrive home?
d Calculate John's speed in kilometres per hour.

4 Copy the axes below onto graph paper.

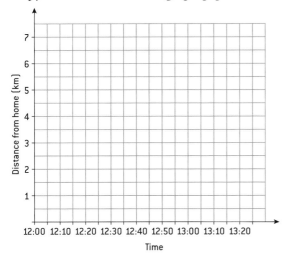

Aaron leaves his house at 12.00 and cycles into town. After 2.5 km he stops at 12.10 to answer his phone. At 12.15 he proceeds into town cycling the remaining 3.5 km at an average speed of 10 km/h. He spends 20 minutes in town and then cycles home without stopping. He arrives home at 13.20.
a Show this journey on a distance–time graph.
b What was Aaron's average speed on the journey home from the town?

5   The height of a ball above ground level is given by the formula $H = 4t - t^2$.

   a   Copy and complete the table of values for t and H.

t (seconds)	0	1	2	3	4
H (metres)					

   b   Draw the graph of H against t.
   c   What was the maximum height reached by the ball?
   d   From the graph find the two times when the ball is 3 metres above the ground.

6   The average temperature of a family-size frozen meal is given by the formula $T = x^2 - 16$ where x ($0 < x \leq 8$) is the number of minutes the meal is placed in the microwave and T is the temperature in °C.

   a   Copy and complete the table of values for x and T.

x (minutes)	0	1	2	3	4	5	6	7	8
T (temperature °C)									

   b   Draw the graph of T against x.
   c   What was the average temperature of the meal when it was taken from the freezer.
   d   Mary wants the meal heated to a temperature of 40 °C. Estimate how long she will need to place the meal in the microwave.

7   A radioactive substance is decaying. Its half-life is 12 years. In 2010 the mass is 160 g.

   a   Draw a graph to show the mass of the substance over the next 60 years.
   b   Use your graph to estimate the time when the mass will be 50 g.

8   A population of rabbits doubles every 3 months. The initial population is 10 rabbits.

   a   Draw a graph to show the population of rabbits over the next 12 months.
   b   Use your graph to estimate the population of rabbits after 5 months.
   c   Use your graph to work out when the population passes 50 rabbits. Give your answer to the nearest month.

CHAPTER 28 Simultaneous equations

This chapter is about

- solving two simultaneous linear equations graphically
- solving two simultaneous linear equations algebraically
- solving problems by forming and solving simultaneous equations
- solving two simultaneous equations where one is linear and the other is not linear
- understanding the geometrical significance of simultaneous equations.

Exercise A

1

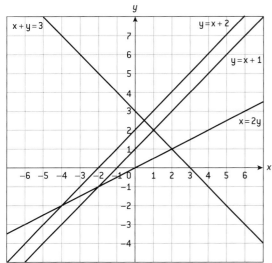

a Use the graph to write down the solutions of the simultaneous equations.

   i $y = x + 1$ **ii** $x = 2y$ **iii** $y = x + 1$ **iv** $y = x + 2$

       $x + y = 3$ $x + y = 3$ $x = 2y$ $x = 2y$

b Explain why there are no solutions for the simultaneous equations.

    $y = x + 1$

    $y = x + 2$

2 On graph paper, draw a set of axes with values of x from 0 to 5 and values of y from -2 to 14. Draw $y = x + 2$ and $y = 3x - 2$. At what point do the lines intersect?

3 On graph paper, draw a set of axes with values of x from 0 to 5 and values of y from -2 to 20. Solve the simultaneous equations $y = 4x - 1$ and $x + y = 4$ using their graphs.

4 On graph paper, draw a set of axes with values of x from 0 to 5 and values of y from -3 to 7. Solve the simultaneous equations $2x + y = 7$ and $2y = x + 3$ graphically.

5 The equations for the sides of a triangle are $x + 2y = 8$, $2y = x$ and $x + 4y = 18$. Find the vertices of the triangle using graphs.

Exercise B

Solve these simultaneous equations.

1 $2x + 5y = 48$
$2x + y = 8$

2 $2x + y = 8$
$3x - y = 17$

3 $x + 3y = 13$
$2x + y = 11$

4 $4x - 3y = 1$
$x + y = -5$

5 $5x + y = 10$
$3x - 5y = 10$

6 $2x + 3y = 17$
$3x + 4y = 24$

7 $5x - 2y = 34$
$3x + 5y = 8$

8 $x - 3y = -5$
$3x - 2y = 6$

9 $4x - 5y = 7$
$4x + y = -11$

10 $2y = 4 - 3x$
$4y + x = 13$

11 $4x = 11 + 3y$
$y = 5x - 22$

12 $4x - 3y + 3 = 0$
$2x + 5y = 18$

13 $x = 2y - 1$
$3x - 4y = 6$

14 $4x + 2y = 2$
$3y = 19 + 2x$

15 $2x - 7y = 43$
$5x - 4y = 13$

16 $6x = 7y + 71$
$2(5x - 4y) = 89$

Exercise C

1 Two numbers, x and y, have a sum of 40 and a difference of 14. Write down two equations in x and y and solve them to find the numbers.

2 The line $y = mx + c$ passes through the points $(-2, 2)$ and $(4, 1)$. Write down two equations and solve them to find m and c. Hence write down the equation of the line.

3 Tickets for the cinema cost £a for adults and £c for children. Mr and Mrs Kennedy go to the cinema with their four children. The total cost is £27. Mrs Jones takes her three children. The total cost is £17. Write down two equations in a and c and solve them to find the cost of an adult ticket and of a child ticket.

4 Pens cost p pence and rulers cost r pence. Jack bought three pens and two rulers. The total cost was £1.35. Jenny bought four pens and three rulers. The total cost was £1.90. Write down two equations in p and r and solve them to find the cost of a pen and of a ruler.

5 For a coach trip the adult fare is twice the child fare. The total fare for two adults and three children is £84. Write down two equations and solve them to find the cost of each fare.

6 **a** The total of Lan's age and his mother's age is 46. If Lan's age is x years and his mother's age is y years, write down an equation in x and y.
   b Next year Lan's mother will be three times as old as Lan. Write down a second equation in x and y. Simplify this equation.
   c Solve your two equations to find both ages.

7 The time T (minutes) taken to cook a turkey is given by the formula $T = a + bM$ where M is the mass of the turkey in kg. A 10 kg turkey takes 3 hours and 50 minutes to cook, whilst an 8 kg turkey takes 3 hours and 10 minutes to cook. How long will it take to cook a 12 kg turkey?

8 A taxi fare has a fixed charge and an additional cost per mile. A girl who travelled 12 miles was charged £13.20, whilst a boy who travelled 15 miles was charged £15.90. What will the fare be for a journey of 24 miles?

Exercise D

1 **a** Draw the graph of $y = x^2 - 6x + 8$ for $x = 0$ to 6.
   b On the same grid, draw the line $y = 2x - 5$.
   c Write down the coordinates of the points where the curve and the line intersect.

2 Use the graph of $y = x^2 - 6x + 8$ from question **1**. By drawing another line on the graph, solve the simultaneous equations $y = x^2 - 6x + 8$ and $2y + x = 8$ graphically.

3 Solve each pair of simultaneous equations algebraically. Where necessary give your solutions correct to 3 significant figures.

   a $y + x - 3 = 0$
   $y = x^2 + 1$

   b $y = x^2 + 3x - 1$
   $x - 2y - 4 = 0$

   c $x + y = 3$
   $4x - y^2 = 0$

   d $y - x = 5$
   $y = x^2 + 1$

   e $y(x + 1) = 10$
   $y = 2x + 3$

   f $2y + 3x = 5$
   $x^2 + 2y^2 = 11$

   g $xy = 8$
   $3y - 2x = -2$

   h $3x + 4y = 10$
   $2x^2 - 5xy - 3 = 0$

   i $x^2 + y^2 = 2$
   $y - 2x - 1 = 0$

   j $2x^2 + 3y = 12$
   $x - y + 1 = 0$

CHAPTER 29

Graphical solution of equations

This chapter is about

- understanding the significance of points of intersection of graphs in the context of solving equations
- determining the lines that need to be drawn on a graph in order to solve a particular equation
- solving a variety of equations using a particular graph
- determining the equation of a function whose solution is a particular point of intersection.

1 **a** Draw the graph of $y = x^2 - 2x - 8$ for values of x from -3 to 5.
   b Use your graph to solve
      i $x^2 - 2x - 8 = 0$.
      ii $x^2 - 2x - 8 = 5$.
      iii $x^2 - 2x - 8 = -3$.

2 **a** Draw the graph of $y = 3x^2 - 2x$ for values of x from -3 to 3.
   b Use your graph to find
      i the minimum value of y
      ii the solutions of the equation $3x^2 - 2x = 10$.

3 **a** Draw the graph of $y = \frac{1}{2}x^2 - 2x + 5$ for values of x from -2 to 6.
   b Use your graph to solve these equations.
      i $\frac{1}{2}x^2 - 2x + 5 = 9$
      ii $x^2 - 4x + 10 = 8$

4 **a** Draw the graph of $y = 5x - 2x^2$ for values of x from -2 to 4.
   b Use your graph to find
      i the maximum value of y and the value of x where it occurs
      ii the solutions of the equation $5x - 2x^2 = 0$
      iii the solutions of the equation $3x - 2x^2 = 0$.

5 **a** Draw the graph of $y = x^2 - 5x + 6$ for values of x from 0 to 5.
   b Use your graph to solve these equations.
      i $x^2 - 5x + 6 = 0$.
      ii $x^2 - 5x + 3 = 0$.

6 The table of values below is for the equation $y = x^2 - x - 4$.

x	−2	−1	0	1	2	3
y	2	−2	−4	−4	−2	2

   a Draw the graph for values of x from -2 to 3.
   b Use your graph to solve these.
      i $x^2 - x - 4 = 0$
      ii $x^2 - x - 1.5 = 0$

7 a Draw the graphs of $y = x^2$ and $y = 5 - \frac{1}{2}x$ for $x = -3$ to 3 on the same grid.

  b What is the equation whose solution is found at the intersection of the two graphs?
  c Use your graphs to solve this equation.

8 a Draw the graph of $y = 2x^2 + 3x - 9$ for values of x from -3 to 2.
  b Use your graph to solve these equations.
    i $2x^2 + 3x - 9 = -1$
    ii $2x^2 + 3x - 4 = 0$

9 a Draw the graph of $y = x^2 - 4x$ for $x = -3$ to 3.
  b Draw a straight line graph on the same grid so that you can solve the equation $x^2 - 5x + 3 = 0$.
  c Use your graphs to solve the equation.

10 a Draw the graph of $y = x^2 - 5x + 3$ for values of x from -2 to 8.
  b Use your graph to solve these equations.
    i $x^2 - 5x + 3 = 0$
    ii $x^2 - 5x - 2 = 0$
    iii $x^2 - 7x + 3 = 0$

11 a Draw the graph of $y = x^2 - 3x$ from $x = -2$ to 5.
  b Use your graph to solve these equations.
    i $x^2 - 3x - 2 = 0$
    ii $x^2 - 4x + 1 = 0$

Do not draw the graphs in questions **12** to **14**.

12 The intersection of two graphs is the solution to the equation $x^2 - 2x - 3 = 0$.

One of the graphs is $y = x^2 - x - 1$. What is the other graph?

13 The graphs of $y = x^2 + 2x$ and $y = 2x + 1$ are drawn on the same grid.

What is the equation whose solution is found at the intersection of the two graphs?

14 The graph of $y = x^2 - 3x - 7$ is drawn on a grid.

What is the equation of the straight line graph that you would draw to solve each of these using the graph of $y = x^2 - 3x - 7$?

  a $x^2 - 5x + 1 = 0$ **b** $x^2 + x - 5 = 0$ **c** $x^2 - 2x = 6$

This chapter is about

- knowing how to read and write inequalities
- displaying and interpreting inequalities on a number line
- solving inequalities
- solving problems involving inequalities
- identifying a region satisfied by a number of inequalities
- finding the inequalities that define a region
- finding the maximum or minimum value of a function subject to the constraints of a given set of inequalities.

Exercise A

1   Write down the integers which satisfy the following.
   a $2 < x < 5$ **b** $3 \leqslant x < 7$ **c** $-2 \leqslant x \leqslant 1$
   d $-8 < x \leqslant -6$ **e** $-4 < x < -1$ **f** $-5 \leqslant x < -4$

2   Write down the integers which satisfy the following.

   a $-3\dfrac{1}{2} \leqslant x \leqslant -1$ **b** $\dfrac{7}{2} \leqslant x \leqslant \dfrac{11}{2}$ **c** $\dfrac{5}{3} < x < \dfrac{20}{3}$

   d $-\dfrac{11}{4} < x \leqslant \dfrac{7}{6}$ **e** $-\dfrac{20}{7} \leqslant x \leqslant -\dfrac{6}{5}$ **f** $-4\dfrac{1}{4} \leqslant x < 2\dfrac{2}{5}$

3   Given that n is an integer write down the smallest value that n can have given that $n > 2$.

4   Given that n is an integer write down the largest value that n can have given that $n \leqslant -3$.

5   Write down the inequality that is represented by each of the number lines.
   a

   b

   c

   d
   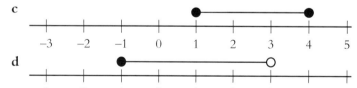

6 Show each of these inequalities on a number line.

  a $x > 4$ **b** $x \leqslant -1$ **c** $-3 < x \leqslant 2$ **d** $-5 < x < -2$

7 Solve each inequality.

  a $2x + 1 \leqslant 6$

  b $3x - 6 \geqslant 0$

  c $7 \leqslant 2x - 1$

  d $5x < x + 12$

  e $4x \geqslant x + 9$

  f $4 + x < 0$

  g $3x + 1 \leqslant 2x + 6$

  h $2(x - 3) > x$

  i $5(x + 1) > 3x + 10$

  j $7x + 5 \leqslant 2x + 30$

  k $5x + 2 < 7x - 4$

  l $3(3x + 2) \geqslant 2(x + 10)$

  m $5 - 3x > 8$

  n $2(3 - x) \leqslant x$

  o $3 - 6x > 2x + 14$

  p $-2 < 2x < 14$

  q $1 < 3x + 1 \leqslant 10$

  r $-8 \leqslant 4(2x - 3) \leqslant 12$

  s $-1 < 5(3x + 1) < 5$

  t $2x + 4 \leqslant 3x - 2 < x + 18$

Exercise B

In questions 1 to 10, label the required region using the letter R.

1 Draw a set of axes and label them from −5 to 5 for x and y.
  Shade the region $x \geqslant -3$.

2 Draw a set of axes and label them from −5 to 5 for x and y.
  Shade the region $y > x$.

3 Draw a set of axes and label them from −5 to 5 for x and y.
  Shade the region $x + y \leqslant 3$.

4 Draw a set of axes and label them from −3 to 3 for x and −5 to 5 for y.
  Shade the region $y \leqslant 2x - 1$.

5 Draw a set of axes and label them from −2 to 6 for x and y.
  Shade the region $4x + 3y < 12$.

6 Draw a set of axes and label them from −3 to 7 for x and y.
  Show, by shading, the region where $x > -2$, $y < 4$ and $y > 2x + 1$.

7 Draw a set of axes and label them from −5 to 5 for x and y.
  Show, by shading, the region where $x < 4$, $y < 3$ and $y \geqslant -x$.

8 Draw a set of axes and label them from 0 to 7 for x and y.
  Show, by shading, the region where $x \geqslant 0$, $y \geqslant 0$ and $3x + y \leqslant 6$.

9 Draw a set of axes and label them from −3 to 5 for x and y.
  Show, by shading, the region where $x \geqslant -1$, $y \geqslant 0$ and $x + 2y \leqslant 4$.

10 Draw a set of axes and label them from −2 to 8 for x and y.
  Show, by shading, the region where $x \geqslant 1$, $x + y > 5$ and $y > 2x + 1$.

11 In each part of this question, write down the inequality that describes the shaded region R.

a
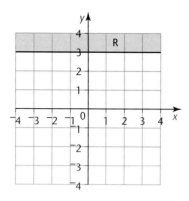

b
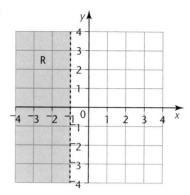

c
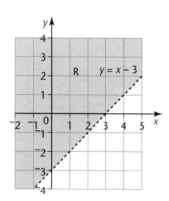

d
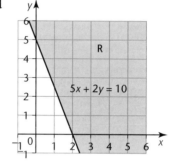

12 Find the set of inequalities which defines each of the regions *R*.

a
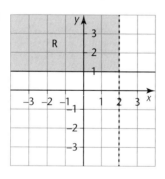

b
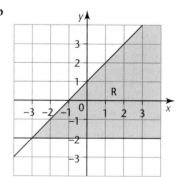

c

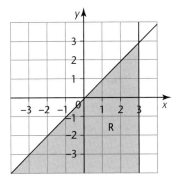

d

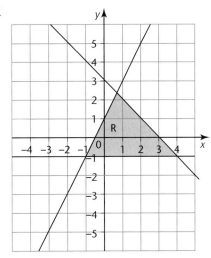

Exercise C

1 Find the coordinates of the point with integer values which
  a maximises the function $3x - 2y$ for the region R
  b minimises the function $x + 4y$ for the region R.

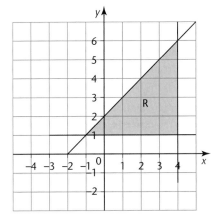

2 Find the point with integer coordinates in the region R defined by the 3 inequalities

$$y \leqslant 2x + 1 \qquad x + y \leqslant 4 \qquad y \geqslant -1$$

which

  a maximises the function $4x + 3y$
  b minimises the function $2x - y$.

Angles in circles

This chapter is about

- knowing the names of the different parts of a circle
- knowing the properties of circles
- proving the properties of circles
- using the properties of circles to calculate angles.

Exercise A

1 Draw a circle with centre O. Mark four points A, B, C, D on the circumference of the circle as shown in the diagram.

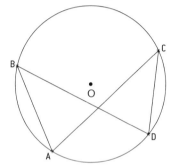

Measure angle ABD and angle ACD. Write a sentence relating your findings.

2 Draw a circle with centre O. Join O to a point C on the circumference. Draw a tangent to the circle at point C. Label it MN. Measure angle MCO. Write a sentence relating your findings.

3 Draw a circle with centre O. Mark four points P, Q, R, S on the circumference of the circle. Join them to form a quadrilateral. Measure angle PQR. Measure angle PSR. Write a sentence relating your findings.

4 Draw a circle with centre O. Draw a diameter in your circle FG. Join F and G to a third point P on the circumference of your circle. Measure angle FPG. Write a sentence relating your findings.

5 Prove that POR = 2PQR. O is the centre of the circle. P, Q and R are points on the circumference of the circle. Let PQO = x and RQO = y

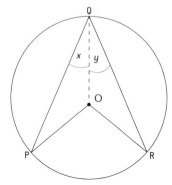

In each of the following diagrams, O is the centre of the circle.
Find the size of each of the lettered angles.
Give reasons for your answers.

6

7

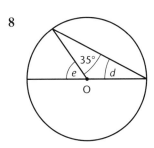

8

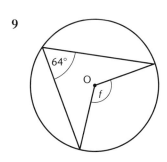

9

10

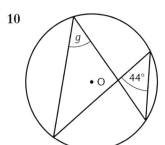

11

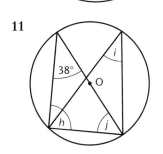

12

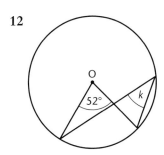

13

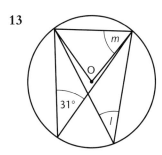

Exercise B

In each of the following diagrams, O is the centre of the circle.
Calculate the size of each of the lettered angles.
Give reasons for your answers.

1

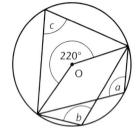

4

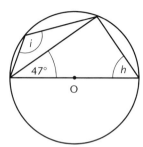

2

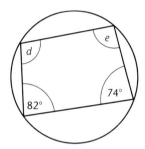

5

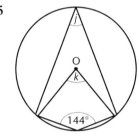

3

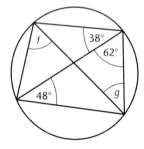

6

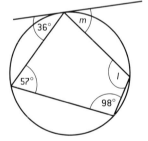

Exercise C

In questions 1 to 4, calculate the size of the angles marked with letters. O is the centre of each circle. X and Y are the points of contact of the tangents to each circle.

1

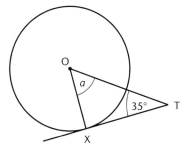

2

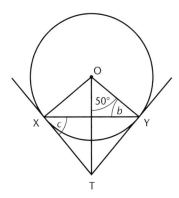

3

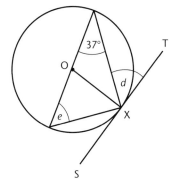

4

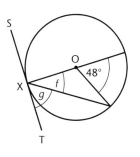

In questions **5** and **6**, find the lengths marked with letters.

5

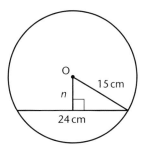

6

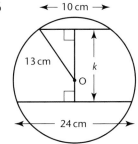

7 TB and TD are tangents to the circle, which has centre O.
Angle APC = $x°$.
Find the size of angle ATC in terms of x.

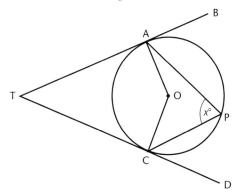

Exercise D

In these questions, ST is a tangent to the circle, which has centre O.
Find the size of the lettered angles, giving reasons for your answers.

1

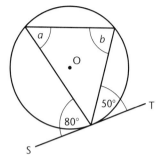

4

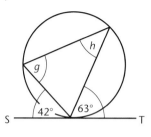

2

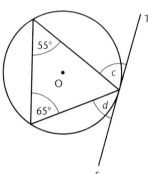

5

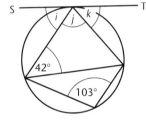

3

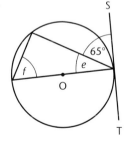

6

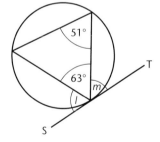

Exercise E

In each of the following diagrams, O is the centre of the circle. Find the size of each of the lettered angles, giving reasons for your answers.

1

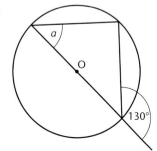

2

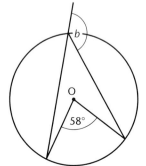

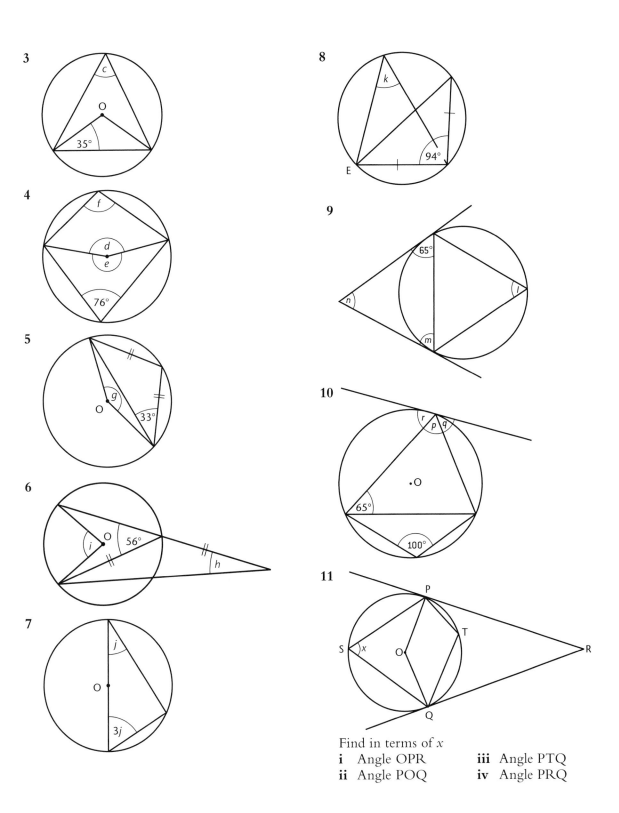

3

4

5

6

7

8

9

10

11

Find in terms of x
i Angle OPR   **iii** Angle PTQ
ii Angle POQ   **iv** Angle PRQ

This chapter is about

- knowing the names of polygons with 5, 6, 7, 8, 9 and 10 sides
- knowing that all the sides are equal in a regular polygon and that all the angles are equal
- knowing that an interior angle and an exterior angle at a vertex add up to 180°
- knowing that the sum of the exterior angles is 360°
- knowing that the sum of the interior angles of a n-sided polygon is 180° × $(n - 2)$
- finding the number of sides in a regular polygon if you know each angle
- finding the angles in a regular polygon if you know the number of sides
- finding the angle at the centre of a regular polygon
- finding the missing angles in an irregular polygon.

Find the missing angles in each of the polygons in questions **1** to **3**.

1

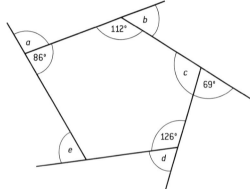

2

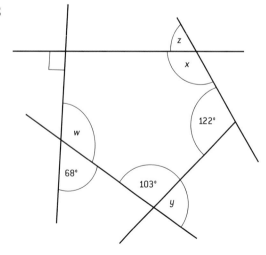

3

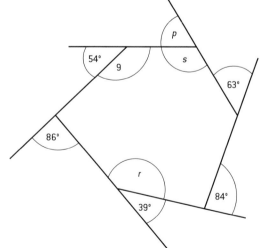

4 A regular polygon has 18 sides. Find the size of each of its exterior and interior angles.

5 A regular polygon has 24 sides. Find the size of each of its exterior and interior angles.

6 A regular polygon has an exterior angle of 12°. How many sides does it have?

7 A regular polygon has an interior angle of 172°. How many sides does it have?

8 Name the regular polygon which has interior angles of 140°.

9 Two sides of a regular pentagon PQRST are produced to meet at M. Calculate the size of the angle M.

10 A polygon has nine sides. Work out the sum of the interior angles of this polygon.

11 A polygon has 13 sides. Work out the sum of the interior angles of this polygon.

12 Four of the exterior angles of a hexagon are 93°, 50°, 37° and 85°. The other two angles are equal.
   a Find the size of these equal exterior angles.
   b Find the size of each interior angle.

13 Four of the exterior angles of a pentagon are 170°, 80°, 157° and 75°.
   a Find the size of the other interior angle.
   b Find the size of each exterior angle.

14 The angles in a heptagon are $2x$, $2x + 10$, $2x$, 140, 135, $2x + 30$ and $2x - 5$. Calculate the value of x.

15 The interior angle sum of a polygon is 2520°. How many sides does the polygon have?

16 Each angle at the centre of a regular polygon is 24°. Calculate the sum of the interior angles of the polygon.

17 Is it possible to have a regular polygon with interior angle 164°? Explain your answer.

18 ABCDEF is a regular hexagon. Calculate each of the angles in the triangle ACD.

19 The angle at the centre of a regular polygon is x. Write an expression in terms of x for the number of sides that the polygon has.

20 Joseph measured all the interior angles of a polygon. His total was 1901° but he had missed an angle.
   a How many sides does the polygon have?
   b What was the missing angle?

21 A square and two other identical regular polygons meet at a point. What type of polygons are these? Justify your answer.

CHAPTER 33

Pythagoras and trigonometry

This chapter is about

- using Pythagoras' theorem to find missing sides
- applying Pythagoras' theorem to solve problems in 2D
- using trigonometry to find missing sides
- using trigonometry to find missing angles
- applying trigonometry to solve problems in 2D
- applying Pythagoras' theorem and trigonometry to solve problems in 3D.

Exercise A

Write an equation relating the sides of each of these triangles.

1

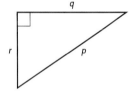

2

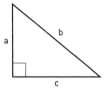

3

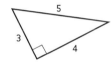

Calculate the missing area of the squares shown in each of these diagrams.

4

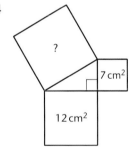

5

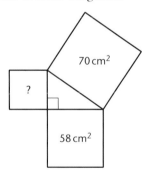

Find the length of the hypotenuse, x, in each of these triangles. Give your answers either exactly or correct to 2 decimal places.

6

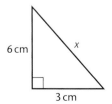

7

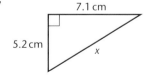

8

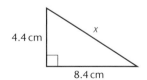

9 PQR is a right-angled triangle. PQ = 13 cm, QR = 7 cm and angle PQR = 90°. Calculate the length of PR.

10 WXY is a right-angled triangle. WX = 12 cm, XY = 9 cm and angle WXY = 90°. Calculate the length of WY.

Find the length marked x in each of these triangles. Give your answers either exactly or correct to 2 decimal places.

11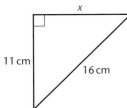

12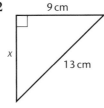

13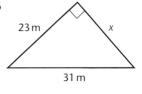

14 ABC is a right-angled triangle. AB = 4.2 cm, AC = 14.81 cm and angle ABC = 90°. Calculate the length of BC.

15 KLM is a right-angled triangle. KL = 19.14 cm, KM = 18 cm and angle KML = 90°. Calculate the length of LM.

16 Ann can walk home from school along two roads or along a path across a field.

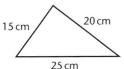

How much shorter is her journey if she takes the path across the field?

17 This network is made of wire. What is the total length of wire?

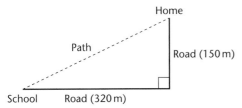

18 A ladder 10 m long has its base 3 m from the foot of a vertical wall. How far up the wall will the ladder reach?

19 The sides of a rectangle are 5 cm and 6 cm long. Find the length of the diagonal of the rectangle.

20 An aircraft flies 120 km South, then 150 km East, then 200 km North. How far is the aircraft from its starting position?

21 State whether or not each of these triangles is right-angled. Explain your reasoning.

a   **b**

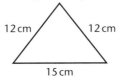

Exercise B

Copy and label each of the three sides in these triangles with the letters O, A and H.

1
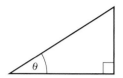

2
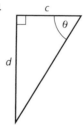

Find the trig ratio connecting the given sides and angle θ in these triangles.

3
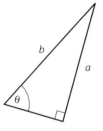

4
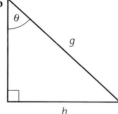

5
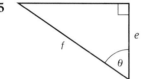

6
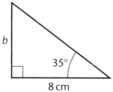

In these diagrams find the lengths marked with a letter. Give your answers to 3 significant figures.

7
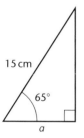

8
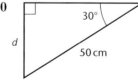

9

10

11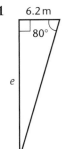
6.2 m
80°
e

12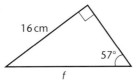
16 cm
57°
f

13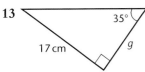
35°
17 cm
g

14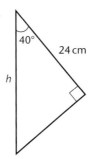
40°
24 cm
h

In these diagrams find the size of the angles marked with a letter. Give all answers to 3 significant figures.

15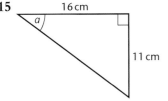
16 cm
a
11 cm

16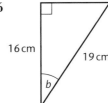
16 cm
19 cm
b

17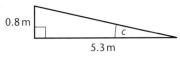
0.8 m
c
5.3 m

18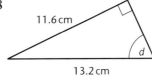
11.6 cm
d
13.2 cm

In these diagrams find the lengths marked with a letter. Give your answers to 3 significant figures.

19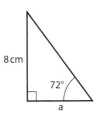
8 cm
72°
a

20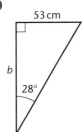
53 cm
b
28°

21

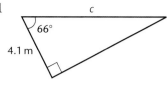

22

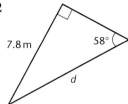

In these diagrams find the size of the angles marked with a letter. Give all answers to 3 significant figures.

23

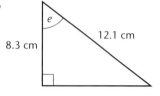

24

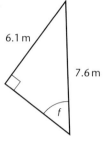

25 ABC is a right-angled triangle in which angle CAB = 90°. AB = 28 cm. Angle ACB = 41°. Calculate the length of BC.

26 PQR is a right-angled triangle in which angle PQR = 90°. PQ = 65 m, QR = 102 m. Calculate angle PRQ.

Exercise C

1 The diagram shows the side view of a bin.

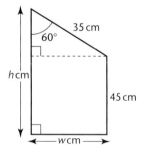

  a Find the width, w cm, of the bin.
  b Find the height, h cm, of the bin.

2 Look at this triangle.

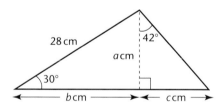

  a Find the height, a cm, of the triangle.
  b Find the length, b cm.
  c Find the length, c cm.
  d Find the area of the triangle.

3 A ship sails on a bearing of 125° for 220 km.
  a Find how far east the ship has travelled.
  b Find how far south the ship has travelled.

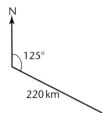

4 Calculate the area of this trapezium.

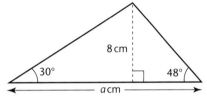

5 The diagram shows a step ladder. The two sections of the ladder are opened to 30°. The feet of the two sections are 1.2 m apart.

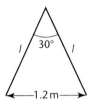

Calculate the length, *l*, of each section of the ladder.

6 a Find the length of the base, *a* cm, of the triangle.

  Give your answer to 2 d.p.

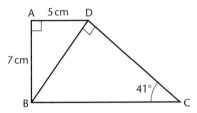

  b Find the area of the triangle.

7 The bearing of A from B is 230°. A is 20 km west of B.

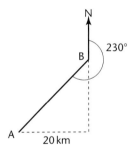

Calculate how far A is south of B.

8 Look at this diagram.

A 5 cm D

7 cm

41°

B   C

Calculate the length of BC.

9 A rectangle has length 12 cm and width 8 cm. Calculate the size of the angle that the diagonal makes with the longer side.

10 A yacht sails from A to B. B is 43 km east of A and 25 km south of A.

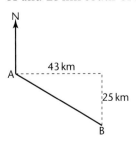

Calculate the bearing of B from A.

11 The diagram shows an isosceles triangle.

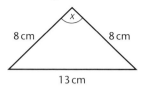

Calculate the size of the angle *x*.

12 A ship sails for 200 miles from A to B on a bearing of 080°. How far north and east of A is the ship when it reaches B?

Exercise D

1 ABCDEFGH is a cuboid with dimensions as shown.

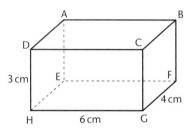

Calculate these.
a AC
b Angle BAC
c AG
d Angle CAG

2 PABCD is a square-based pyramid with P vertically above the midpoint of the square base.

AB = 12 cm, AP = BP = CP = DP = 15 cm.

E is the midpoint of BC. F is the midpoint of AD.

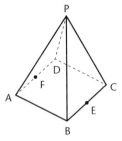

Calculate these.
a DB
b Angle PBD
c PE
d Angle PEF

3 ABCDEF is a triangular prism with angle BCF = 90°.

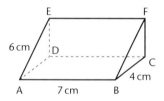

Calculate these.
a FC
b Angle FBC
c EB
d Angle EBD

4 PABCD is a square-based pyramid with P vertically above the midpoint of the square base.

AP = BP = CP = DP = 9.5 cm. BC = 5.8 cm.

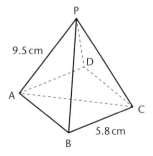

Calculate angle PAC.

5 A pencil case is a cuboid with a base measuring 6 cm by 15 cm. A pencil 17 cm long just fits in the box.

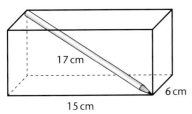

17 cm

15 cm

6 cm

Calculate the height of the pencil case.

6 The points A, B and C are in the same horizontal plane. The angle of elevation of a vertical mast MC from A is 24.7°. AC is 34 m and BC is 57 m.

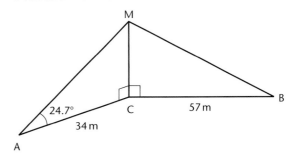

Find the angle of elevation of M from B.

7 A cuboid has a base with sides 5.6 cm by 8.2 cm. Its height is 4.3 cm.

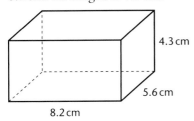

4.3 cm

5.6 cm

8.2 cm

Calculate the angle between a space diagonal of the cuboid and
a the base
b a 5.6 cm by 4.3 cm face.

8 A pyramid is 8 cm high and has a square base with sides of 6 cm. Its sloping edges are all of equal length. Calculate the angle between a sloping edge and the base.

9 A square-based pyramid has a height of 8.3 cm. Its sloping faces each make an angle of 55° with the base.
a Find the length of the sides of the base.
b Find the length of the sloping edges of the pyramid.

10 ABCDEF is a triangular wedge. The base ABFE is a horizontal rectangle. C is vertically above B.

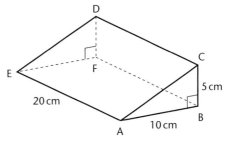

D

E

F

C

5 cm

20 cm

A

10 cm

B

a Calculate the length AD.
b Calculate the angle which AD makes with
  i the base ABFE.
  ii the face ABC.

CHAPTER 34

Similarity

This chapter is about

- knowing the definition of similar figures
- calculating missing lengths in similar figures
- proving that two triangles are similar
- knowing the relationship between the ratios of length, area and volume of similar figures
- using the relationship between the ratios of length, area and volume of similar figures to calculate lengths, areas and volumes.

Exercise A

1 Explain why these trapeziums are not similar.

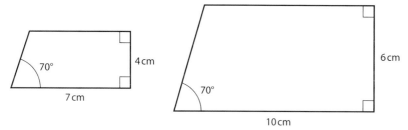

2 Look at these two triangles.

Explain why the triangles are similar.

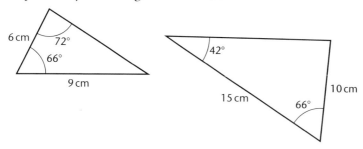

3 State, with reasons, which of these rectangles are similar.

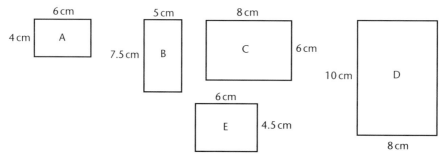

4 Any two squares must be similar. Write down the names of three other types of shapes for which this statement is true.

5 These two rectangles are similar. Calculate x.

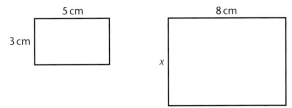

6 These two parallelograms are similar. Calculate the length marked x.

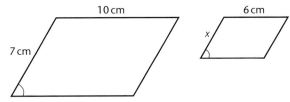

7 The triangles PQR and STU are similar. Calculate the lengths of ST and SU.

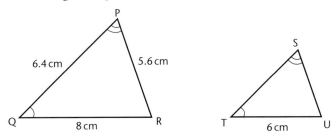

8 The triangles ABC and DEF are similar. Calculate the lengths of AB and EF.

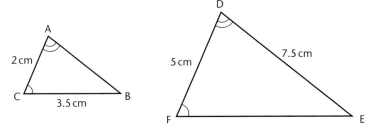

9 The quadrilaterals ABCD and PQRS are similar.

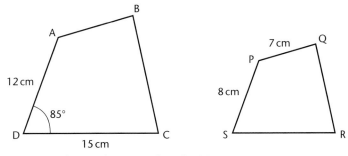

   a Write down the size of angle PSR.
   b Calculate the lengths of AB and SR.

10 Decide if each pair of triangles is similar or not. You must explain your answer fully, commenting on the angles or the ratios of the corresponding sides.

a

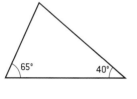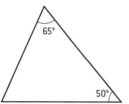

b

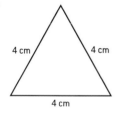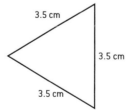

c

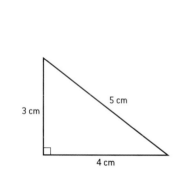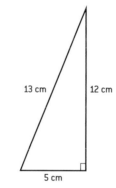

d

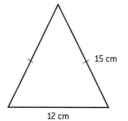

e

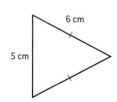

Exercise B

Remember to give reasons when stating that two angles are equal.

1 Prove that triangle ABC is similar to triangle ADE.

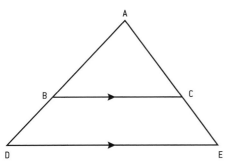

2 Prove that triangle MON is similar to triangle POQ.

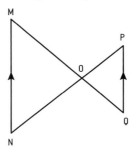

3 Prove that triangle FGH is similar to triangle GHI.

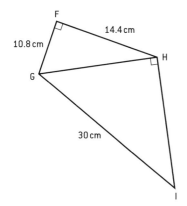

4 Prove that triangle JKL is similar to triangle KTL.

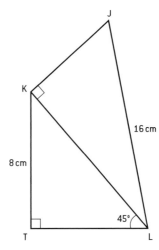

Find each missing length.

5

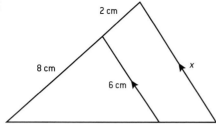

6

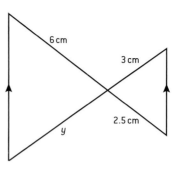

7

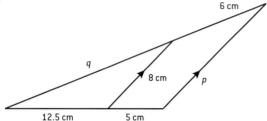

8

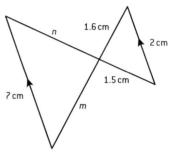

9

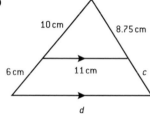

10 An oval mirror has an area of $162\,\text{cm}^2$.
What is the area of a similar mirror which is one and a half times as long?

11 The three tables in a nesting set of tables are similar, with heights in the ratio $1:1.2:1.5$.
The area of the smallest table top is $120\,\text{cm}^2$. What is the area of the middle-sized table top?

12 A model of a theatre set is made to a scale of $1:20$.
A cupboard on the model has a volume of $50\,\text{cm}^3$.
Find the volume of the cupboard on the actual set, giving your answer in m^3.

13 Two jugs are similar, with capacities of 1 litre and 2 litres respectively. The height of the larger jug is $14.8\,\text{cm}$.
What is the height of the smaller jug, to the nearest millimetre?

14 Julia is making a model of a wooden statue. She uses the same kind of wood as the original.
The model is on a scale of $1:20$.
   a The statue is 15 m high. How high will Julia's model be?
   b 500 litres of varnish were needed for the statue. How many litres will be needed for the model?
   c Julia's model weighs 3 kg. Estimate the weight of the statue.

15 LEGO® and DUPLO® are types of building bricks for children.
Duplo bricks are designed for younger children and are twice as large as Lego bricks.

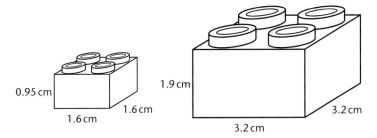

  a Janet makes a shape using Duplo bricks. Her shape is 9.5 cm high. Elaine makes a similar
      shape from Lego. How high is Elaine's shape?
  b The area of the base of Elaine's shape is 64 cm². What is the area of the base of Janet's shape?
  c The volume of Elaine's shape is 304 cm³. What is the volume of Janet's shape?

16 This is a set of Russian dolls. The larger dolls are enlargements of the smallest doll.
The heights of the dolls are 3 cm, 4.5 cm and 8 cm respectively.

  a The width of the smallest doll is 1.2 cm.
      What is the width of the largest doll?
  b The surface area of the middle-sized doll is 8.4 cm².
      What is the surface area of the smallest doll?
  c The volume of the smallest doll is 4.2 cm³.
      What is the volume of the middle-sized doll?

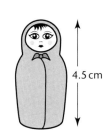
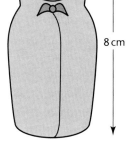

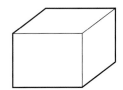

17 These two cuboids are similar.
The volume of the smaller cuboid is 2000 cm³.
The volume of the larger cuboid is 8000 cm³.
The surface area of the smaller cuboid is 1200 cm².
Calculate the surface area of the larger cuboid.

This chapter is about

- knowing when to use the sine rule and the cosine rule
- calculating missing sides and angles using either rule
- knowing how to use the area rule of a triangle.

Exercise A

1 Find x.

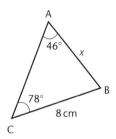

2 Find x.

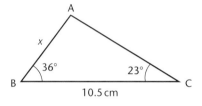

3 ABC is a triangle in which BAC = 58°, ABC = 42° and AC = 6.6 cm. Calculate BC.

4 PQR is a triangle in which QPR = 55°, PQR = 30° and QR = 14 cm. Calculate PQ.

5 Find angle ACB.

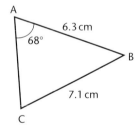

6 Find angle ACB.

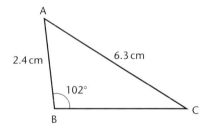

7 PQR is a triangle in which QR = 7 cm, PR = 15 cm and angle PQR = 124°. Calculate angle QPR.

8 ABC is a triangle in which BC = 5.9 cm, AC = 4.7 cm and angle BAC = 106°. Calculate angle BCA.

9 Find length AC.

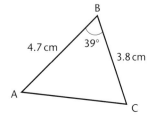

10 Find length AB.

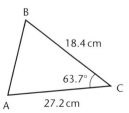

11 ABC is a triangle in which ABC = 120°, BC = 8 cm and AB = 6 cm. Calculate AC.

12 WXY is a triangle in which WXY = 76.5°, XY = 13.4 cm and WX = 19.2 cm. Calculate WY.

13 Find angle CAB.

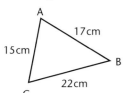

14 Find angle CAB.

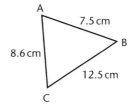

15 PQR is a triangle in which QR = 7.3 cm, PR = 9.2 cm and PQ = 6.5 cm. Calculate the size of angle R.

16 ABC is a triangle in which BC = 5 cm, AC = 9 cm and AB = 6 cm. Calculate the size of the largest angle.

17 Find the area of each of these triangles.

a

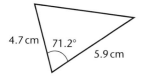

b

18 In triangle ABC, AB = 15.3 cm, AC = 9.6 cm and angle BAC = 53.6°. Find the area of triangle ABC.

19 The area of triangle WXY = 14.1 cm². WX = 6.5 cm and angle WXY = 62°. Calculate XY.

20 The area of triangle JKL = 9.37 m². JK = 5.7 m and KL = 3.6 m. Calculate angle JKL.

Exercise B

1 Find　　　　　**a** Angle A　　　**b** Angle C　　　**c** Side AB.

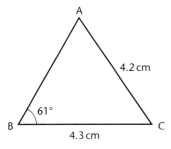

2 In triangle PQR, PQ = 7.8 cm, angle R = 79° and angle P = 51°. Find these.
　　a Side QR
　　b Angle Q
　　c Side PR

3 The angles of elevation of the bottom (B) and top (T) of a flagpole on top of a tower (AB) are 37° and 42°. These are measured 200 m from the base of the tower at a point C.

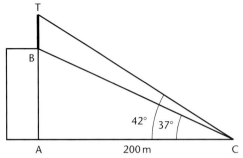

a Find the length BC.
b Find the height of the flagpole, BT.

4 In triangle PQR, PR = 7.2 cm, QR = 6.3 cm and angle PRQ = 37°. Find these.
a The length of PQ
b Angle PQR.

5 The lengths of the sides of triangle ABC are AB = 4.6 cm, BC = 11.5 cm and CA = 7.8 cm. Find the sizes of the angles of the triangle.

6 Find **a** BD **b** AB **c** the area of ABCD.

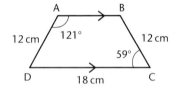

7 A, B and C are points on an orienteering course. The bearing of B from A is 040°. The bearing of C from B is 125°. AB is 3.7 km and BC is 2.3 km.

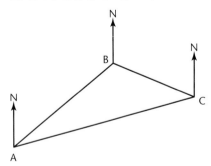

What is the distance AC?

8 ABCD is a kite. Find its area.

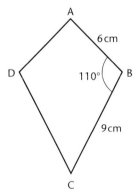

9 In triangle EFG,
EF = 7 m, FG = 9 m and angle G = 39°.
Find these.

  a Angle E

  b Angle F

  c Side EG

10 ABC is a flower bed in a garden.
AB is 3.56 m long.

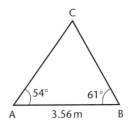

Find the lengths of the other two sides.

11 P, Q and R are three buoys marking a
sailing course. The bearing of P from Q is
035°. The bearing of P from R is 310°. The
bearing of R from Q is 075°. The length of
QR is 5.3 km.

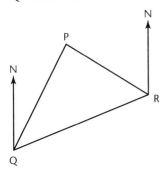

Find the total length of the three stages of
the course from P back to P.

12 Find   **a** BC   **b** AD

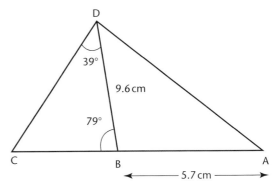

13 ABCD is a children's playground.
OA = 83 m, OB = 122 m, OC = 106 m,
OD = 78 m.

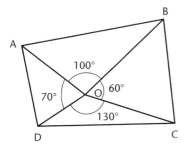

Calculate the area and the perimeter of the
playground.

14 Find angle BAC.

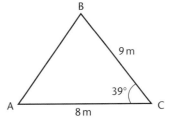

CHAPTER 36

Perimeter, area and volume 1

This chapter is about

- calculating the perimeter and area of a circle and of shapes including circular sections
- calculating the area of a parallelogram and a trapezium
- calculating the surface area and volume of a prism and a cylinder.

Exercise A

For questions 1 to 6, find **a** the perimeter **b** the area

1

4 cm

2 cm

2

6 cm

7 cm

10 cm

8 cm

3

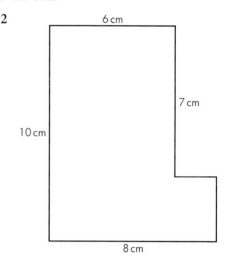

9x

3x

6x

2x

3x

x

All lengths are in cm. Give answers in terms of x in their simplest form.

4

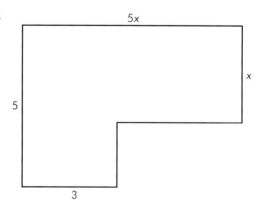

5x

x

5

3

All lengths are in cm. Give answers in terms of x in their simplest form.

5

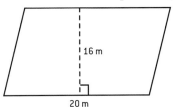

All lengths are in cm. Give answers in terms of x and y in their simplest form.

6

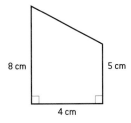

7 Find the area of the parallelogram.

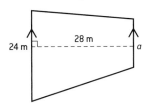

8 Find the area of the trapezium.

9 The area of a parallelogram is $7.56\,\text{m}^2$. Its base is $5.4\,\text{m}$. Calculate the perpendicular height of the parallelogram.

10 The parallel sides of a trapezium are $8\,\text{cm}$ and $11\,\text{cm}$. The area of the trapezium is $42.75\,\text{cm}^2$. Calculate the perpendicular height of the trapezium.

11 Calculate a given that the area is $360\,\text{m}^2$.

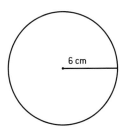

Exercise B

1 Find the circumference of each of the following circles. Give your answers in terms of π.

a

b

2 Find the diameter of the circle with circumference **a** 42π cm **b** 0.8π m

3 Find the radius of the circle with circumference **a** 5π cm **b** 16π m

4 Calculate the circumference of the circles with these diameters, giving your answers correct to 1 decimal place. **a** 8 cm **b** 17 cm **c** 39.2 cm

5 Find the circumference of the circles with these radii, giving your answers correct to 1 decimal place. **a** 78 mm **b** 39 mm **c** 4.4 m

6 Find the diameter of the circle with circumference **a** 14 cm **b** 1.6 m

7 Find the radius of the circle with circumference **a** 8.4 m **b** 10 cm

Give all answers to the following questions correct to 3 significant figures.

8 Find the perimeter of a semicircle with diameter 12 cm.

9 Find the perimeter of a semicircle with radius 1.2 cm.

10 Find the perimeter of a quadrant of a circle with diameter 2.5 m.

11 Find the perimeter of a quadrant of a circle with radius 6 cm.

12 Calculate the perimeter of the shape shown.

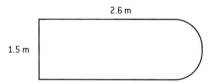

13 Find the area of the circles with these radii. **a** 17 cm **b** 4.3 cm

14 Find the area of the circles with these diameters.
 a 18 cm **b** 3.64 m **c** 2120 mm

15 The area of a circle is 30 cm². Calculate its radius.

16 The area of a circle is 45 m². Calculate its diameter.

17 The area of a circle is 120 cm². Calculate its circumference.

18 The circumference of a circle is 19.48 m. Calculate its area.

19 Find the area of a semicircle with diameter 16 cm.

20 Find the area of a quadrant of a circle with radius 2.4 cm.

21 The area of a semicircle is 72.6 cm². Calculate the perimeter of the semicircle.

22 Calculate **a** the area **b** the perimeter.

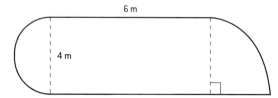

23 A flowerbed is a circle with radius 1.2 m. Mr Green wants to put compost on the flowerbed. The instructions tell him to use 2 litres of compost per square metre. What amount of compost should he use for the flowerbed?

24 A metal plate is a rectangle 8 cm by 12 cm. A circular hole with diameter 5 cm is cut out of the plate. Calculate the area of metal that remains.

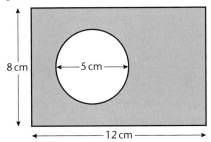

Exercise C

1 Find the volume of a cube with edge 5 cm.

2 Calculate the volume of each cuboid. All measurements are in metres.

a
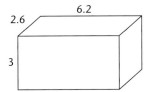

b
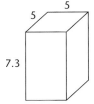

3 A cuboid is 1.2 m by 1.8 m by 2 cm. Calculate its volume
   a in cubic centimetres.   **b** in cubic metres.

4 Find the height of a cuboid which is 15 cm long by 8 cm wide and has a volume of 480 cm³.

5 A wooden block is 10 cm wide, 2 cm long and 4 cm high. How many of these blocks will fill a 1-metre cube?

6 A box is 10 cm high, 5 cm long and 3 cm wide. Calculate the surface area of the box.

7 A biscuit tin is 12 cm long, 5 cm wide and 6 cm deep and has a lid. Calculate the surface area of the tin.

8 The surface area of cuboid is 180 cm². Its length is 8 cm and its breadth is 6 cm. Calculate the volume of the cuboid.

9 The volume of a cube is 512 m³. Calculate the surface area of the cube.

10 Calculate the volume of the shape shown.

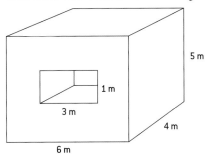

Find the exact volume of each of these prisms.

11

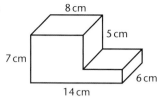

12

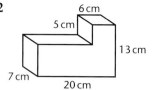

13

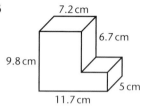

14

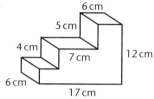

15

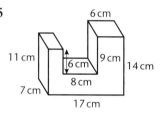

16

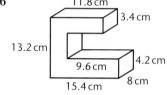

17 Find the volume and surface area of the prism.

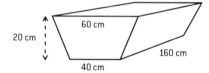

18 The volume of the prism is $0.675\,\text{m}^2$.

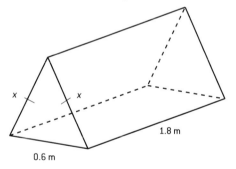

Calculate the length of the sides marked x.

Exercise D

1 Calculate the volume of this cylinder.

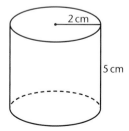

2 The volume of a cylinder is $1000\,\text{cm}^3$. Its radius is $10\,\text{cm}$. Calculate its height.

3 The volume of a cylinder is 250 cm³. Its height is 12.3 cm. Calculate its radius.

4 Find the surface area of the closed cylinder.

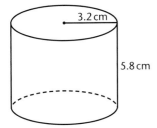

5 Find the surface area of the cylinder open at both ends.

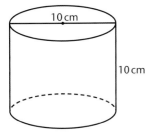

6 This cylinder holds 10 litres. The cross-sectional area is 200 cm². Find the height of the cylinder.

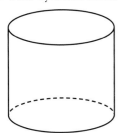

7 Calculate the surface area of the solid shown.

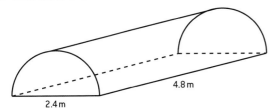

8 The volume of a cylinder is 209 cm³. The height of the cylinder is 6.5 cm. Calculate the radius of the cylinder.

9 The curved surface area of an open cylinder is 72.1 cm². The radius is 1.82 cm. Calculate the height of the cylinder.

10 A circular pond of radius 1.3 m is to be filled with water to a depth of 65 cm. Calculate the volume of water in litres.

CHAPTER 37

Perimeter, area and volume 2

This chapter is about

- calculating the surface area and volume of a prism, cylinder, cone or sphere
- calculating the volume and surface area of a solid made up from two solids
- calculating the length of an arc of a circle
- calculating the area of a sector and a segment of a circle
- distinguishing between formulae for length, area and volume by considering dimensions.

Exercise A

1 For each cone calculate
   i   the curved surface area
   ii the total surface area
   iii the volume.

a

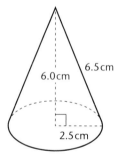

6.0 cm 6.5 cm
2.5 cm

b

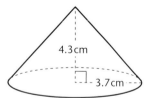

4.3 cm
3.7 cm

c

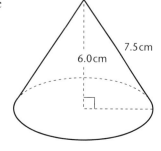

7.5 cm
6.0 cm

d

2.7 cm
10.5 cm

e

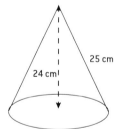

25 cm
24 cm

2 This conical glass holds 150 ml. Its top
   radius is 4 cm.

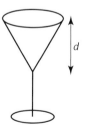

d

Find its depth, *d*.

3 A cone has slant height 15 cm and the area of its base is 254 cm^2.
Find its total surface area.

4 A cone has radius 10 cm and its volume is 2513 cm^3.
Find its curved surface area.

5 The curved surface area of a cone is 754 cm^2 and its slant height is 20 cm.
Find its volume.

6 Work out the volume of each frustum.

a
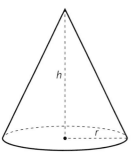

b
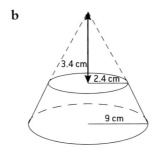

c
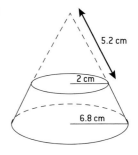

7 Work out the total surface area of each of the frustums in question **6**.

8 A sphere has radius 5 cm. Find
  a its surface area   **b** its volume.

9 A hemisphere has diameter 9 cm. Find
  a its total surface area
  b its volume.

10 A sphere has volume 30 cm^3. Find its surface area.

11 A sphere has surface area 100 cm^2. Find its volume.

12 A football has outer diameter 310 mm and inner diameter 304 mm. Work out the volume of plastic required to manufacture one of these footballs. Give your answer in cm^3.

13 A hemispherical glass bowl has an internal diameter of 22 cm and is 7.5 mm thick throughout.
5% of the original glass is removed when the pattern is cut into the bowl.
Calculate the volume of glass remaining.

14 A cone and a cylinder have equal bases and equal heights.

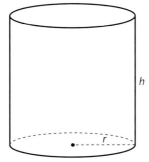

  a If the volume of the cylinder is 36 cm^3, find the volume of the cone.
  b If the volume of the cone is 19 cm^3, find the volume of the cylinder.
  c If the combined volume of both shapes is 64 cm^3, find the volume of the cylinder.

15 A metal sphere of radius 4 cm is melted down and then cast as a cube. What are the dimensions of the cube?

16 A cylindrical glass bowl of radius 15 cm has water in it with floating candles. 20 spherical glass marbles of radius 1.2 cm are placed in the bowl.

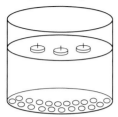

By how much does the water level in the bowl rise?

17 A cone has a base radius of 4.3 cm and perpendicular height of 8.4 cm. It has the same volume as a sphere. Find the radius of the sphere.

18 The diagram shows a cone of radius 4.8 cm attached to a cylinder of height 5.8 cm which is attached to a hemisphere. The total height of the object is 17 cm.

Calculate
a the total volume of the object
b the total surface area of the object.

19 A salt pot is in the form of a hollow cylinder of diameter 3 cm and height 3 cm with a hemispherical shell fixed on top.
Salt is poured into the pot to a depth of 2.5 cm.
The pot is inverted, with the hole covered, so the flat base of the cylinder is horizontal.

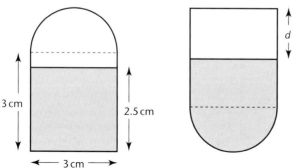

Find the distance, d, from the top of the salt to the flat base of the cylinder.

20 The volume of this frustum is 1422 cm^3.
  a Find the volume of the original cone to 1 decimal place.
  b Find the curved surface area of the frustum.

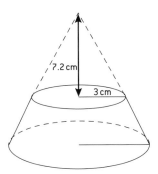

Exercise B

1 Find the arc length of each of these sectors.
  Give your answers to 3 significant figures.

a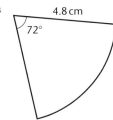
4.8 cm
72°

b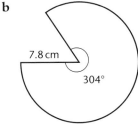
7.8 cm
304°

c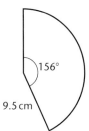
156°
9.5 cm

d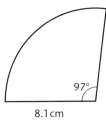
97°
8.1 cm

e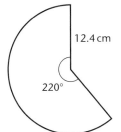
12.4 cm
220°

2 Calculate the area of each of the sectors in question **1**.
  Give your answers to 3 significant figures.

3 Calculate the perimeter of each of these sectors.
  Give your answers to 3 significant figures.

a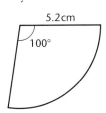
5.2 cm
100°

b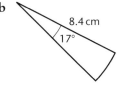
8.4 cm
17°

c
10.7 cm
200°

4 Calculate the sector angle in each of these sectors.
Give your answers to the nearest degree.

a
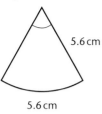
5.6 cm
5.6 cm

b
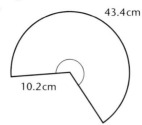
43.4 cm
10.2 cm

c

8.4 cm
6.5 cm

d

3.8 cm
Area = 8.2 cm²

e

Area = 50 cm²
7.3 cm

f
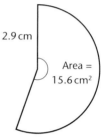
2.9 cm
Area = 15.6 cm²

5 Calculate the radius of each of these sectors.
Give your answers correct to 1 decimal place.

a

8.4 cm
45°

b
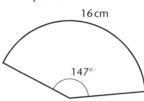
16 cm
147°

c
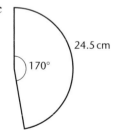
24.5 cm
170°

d

Area = 25 cm²
220°

6 O is the centre of the circle.
Angle AOB = 120°.

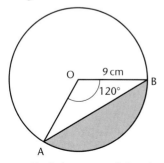
O
9 cm
B
120°
A

a Find the area of the shaded segment.
b Find the perimeter of the shaded segment.

7 O is the centre of the circle. Angle AOB = 74°

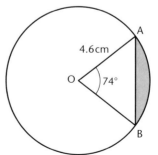
A
4.6 cm
O
74°
B

a Find the area of the shaded segment.
b Find the perimeter of the shaded segment.

8 O is the centre of the circle. Angle AOB = 116°

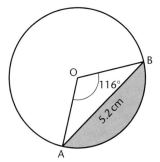

a Find the area of the shaded segment.
b Find the perimeter of the shaded segment.

Exercise C

Work out whether the following expressions are lengths, areas, volumes or none of these, where m, n, p and q are lengths.

1 $2m + 3p$

2 $4nq$

3 πmp

4 $2p(q - n)$

5 $3mq + 5q$

6 $\dfrac{3npq}{m}$

7 $5m^3 + 2\pi np$

8 $\sqrt{n^2 + q^2}$

9 $\sqrt{6\pi p^3}$

10 $8n(p + q)^2$

11 $\dfrac{3pq}{5n}$

12 $\dfrac{6\pi np^2}{q}$

13 $\dfrac{6n - 2q}{3p}$

14 $\sqrt{8mnpq}$

15 $\dfrac{4}{3}\pi(mn - 2p)$

16 $\dfrac{\sqrt{3mn - 3q^2}}{5m}$

17 $3p\sqrt{m^2 - 4q^2}$

18 $2\pi m(3p + q)(5p - n)$

This chapter is about

- using a ruler and compasses to do constructions
- drawing loci
- drawing plans and elevations.

Exercise A

1 a Make an accurate full-size drawing of this triangle.

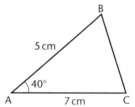

b Measure the length of BC on your diagram.

2 a Make an accurate full-size drawing of this triangle.

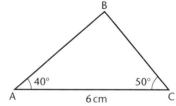

b Measure the length of AB on your drawing.

3 a Make an accurate full-size drawing of this triangle.

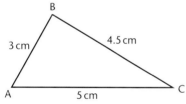

b Measure the angles on your drawing.

4 a Construct the triangle ABC where AB = 7.4 cm, AC = 6.5 cm and angle BAC = 52°.
b Measure BC.

5 a Construct the triangle DEF where DF = 7.7 cm, angle EDF = 48° and angle EFD = 55°.
b Measure DE.

6 a Construct the triangle RST where RS = 5.8 cm, RT = 7.2 cm and ST = 6.3 cm.
b Measure the angle SRT.

7 a Make a scale drawing of the triangle ABC using a scale of 1 cm to 5 m with AB = 25 m, angle CAB = 46°, angle CBA = 71°.
b i Measure the length of BC on your drawing.
ii Write down the actual length of BC.

8 a Draw this triangle accurately.

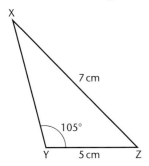

b Measure angle YXZ.

9 AC is the shorter diagonal of a kite.
AC is 4.6 cm.
The sides AB and BC are each 5.8 cm and
the sides AD and CD are each 8.3 cm.

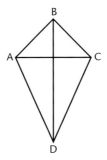

a Draw the kite accurately.
b Measure the length of diagonal BD.
c Calculate the area of the kite.

10 Draw a horizontal line 7.2 cm long and label it AB. Construct the perpendicular bisector of the line AB.

11 Draw a horizontal line 10 cm long and label it XY. Mark the point P that is 4 cm to the right of X and 2 cm above XY. Construct a line perpendicular to XY that passes through P.

12 Draw an angle of 110°. Construct the bisector of the angle.

13 Construct a triangle with sides of length 9 cm, 8 cm and 6 cm.
Construct the bisectors of each of the three angles. What do you notice?

14 Mark a point A. Draw the locus of points which are 3.6 cm from the point A.

15 Draw a line 8 cm long. Draw the locus of points which are 2 cm from the line.

16 Construct a triangle ABC with AB = 10 cm, BC = 8 cm and AC = 5 cm.
Show, by shading, the locus of points which are inside the triangle and closer to A than B.

17 The diagram shows a swimming pool 50 m long by 20 m wide.

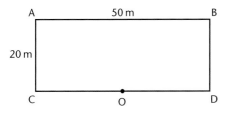

The shallow end extends to a distance 20 m from AC.

Amanda's mother is at O, halfway along CD.
a Using a scale of 1 cm to 5 m, make a scale drawing of the pool.
b Amanda's mother says that Amanda can swim anywhere in the shallow end or within 15 m of her. Show, by shading, all the places that Amanda can swim.

18 Construct a triangle ABC with AB = 11 cm, AC = 7 cm and BC = 9 cm.

Show, by construction, the locus of points inside the triangle which are equidistant from A and B and also nearer to AB than AC.

19 Construct a rectangle ABCD with AB = 10 cm and AD = 6 cm.

Show, by construction, the locus of points inside the rectangle for which all these statements are true.

a The points are nearer to D than A. **b** The points are nearer to DC than DA.

c The points are less than 7 cm from A.

Exercise B

Sketch the plan, front elevation and side elevation of each of the solid shapes in questions **1** to **4**. The arrows indicate the direction of the plan, P, the front elevation, F, and the side elevation, S.

1

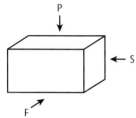

2

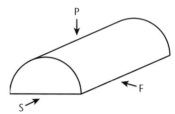

3

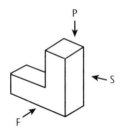

4

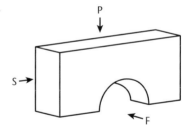

Draw accurately the full-size plan and elevations of each of the solid shapes in questions **5** and **6**.

5

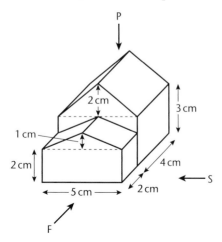

6

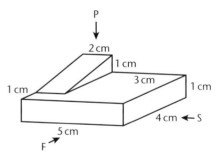

CHAPTER 39

Compound measures

This chapter is about

- knowing the formulae to find speed, distance and time
- using the formulae to find speed, distance and time
- knowing the formulae to find density, mass and volume
- using the formulae to find density, mass and volume
- using other compound measures.

Exercise A

1 Find the average speed in mph for each journey.

   a 70 miles in 2 hours
   b 31 miles in 30 minutes
   c 12.5 miles in 15 minutes
   d 96 miles in $1\frac{1}{2}$ hours
   e 18 miles in 20 minutes
   f 115 miles in 1 hour 40 minutes
   g 23 miles in 12 minutes
   h 1.5 miles in 120 seconds
   i $\frac{1}{4}$ mile in 20 seconds
   j 0.2 miles in $\frac{1}{2}$ second

2 Find the average speed in km/h for each journey.

   a 144 km in 3 hours
   b 11 km in 10 minutes
   c 217 km in $3\frac{1}{2}$ hours
   d 24 km in 40 minutes
   e 64 km in $\frac{3}{4}$ hour
   f 9.4 km in 5 minutes
   g 190 km in 3 hours and 10 minutes
   h 38 km in 24 minutes
   i 2 metres in 3 seconds
   j 8 mm in $\frac{1}{3}$ second

3 Faith travels 28 miles in 35 minutes. Calculate her average speed in mph.

4 Andrew is on a high speed train. It travels 280 miles in $2\frac{1}{2}$ hours.
   Calculate the average speed of the train.

5 Find the time taken to travel 100 miles at an average speed of 60 mph.

6 Find the distance travelled on a journey that took $1\frac{1}{2}$ hours at an average speed of 70 km/h.

7 Barney travels 15 km in 18 minutes. Calculate his average speed in km/h.

8 Copy and complete the following table that shows the average speed, time taken and length of each journey.

	Average speed	Time taken	Length of journey
a	45 mph	30 minutes	
b	74 mph	$1\frac{1}{4}$ hours	
c	50 km/h		180 km
d	60 km/h		54 km
e		45 minutes	75 km
f		8 minutes	12 miles
g	36.4 km/h	6 minutes	
h	48 km/h		1200 m

9 A train leaves the station at 09.10 and arrives at its destination at 10.40. The distance travelled is 84 miles. Find the train's average speed.

10 A car leaves Omagh at 4.25 p.m. and travels 14 miles to Ballygawley. It arrives at Ballygawley at 4.45 p.m. Find the average speed of the car for this journey.

11 A bus left Limavady and travelled 12 miles to Coleraine. It left Limavady at 07.45 and travelled at an average speed of 48 mph. What time did it arrive in Coleraine?

12 a Find the average speed of a car which travels 75 km in 1 hour 15 minutes.
   b A car travels 15 km in 14 minutes. Find its average speed in kilometres per hour.
   Give your answer correct to 1 decimal place.

13 A train is travelling at 22 m/s. How far does it travel in $1\frac{3}{4}$ hours? Give your answer in km.

14 A runner's average speed is 3.2 metres per second.
   How long does it take her to run 1.2 km? Give your answer in minutes.

15 Convert each of these speeds to m/s.
   a 36 km/h   **b** 66 km/h   **c** 90 cm/min   **d** 8.28 km/h   **e** 0.9 km/h

16 Convert each of these speeds to km/h
   a 20 m/s   **b** 48 m/s   **c** 0.2 m/s   **d** 12 cm/s   **e** $\frac{1}{3}$ m/s

Exercise B

1 Find the density in g/cm^3 of a substance which has mass 300 g and volume 150 cm^3.

2 Find the density of a substance with mass 1.2 kg and volume 400 cm^3
   a in kg/cm^3 **b** in g/cm^3.

3 A block of density 3.125 g/cm^3 has volume 400 cm^3. Find its mass in grams.

4 A block of density 5.25 g/cm^3 has volume 720 cm^3. Find its mass
   a in grams   **b** in kilograms.

5 A mass of 280 g has density 3.5 g/cm^3. Find its volume.

6 A mass of 3 kg has density 7.5 g/cm^3. Find its volume.

7 Find the density of each object in g/cm³.

a
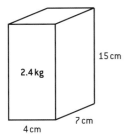
15 cm

2.4 kg

4 cm   7 cm

b
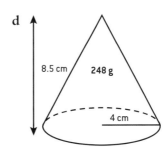
6 cm

4 cm   12.5 kg   18 cm

12 cm

c
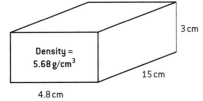
4 cm

750 g   14 cm

d
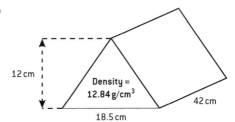
8.5 cm   248 g

4 cm

8 A cuboid measures 8 cm by 6 cm by 2 cm. Its mass is 75 g. Find its density in g/cm³.

9 A cube has sides of length 5 cm. Its mass is 7500 g. Find its density in kg/cm³.

10 Find the mass of each object shown.

a
3 cm

Density = 5.68 g/cm³

15 cm

4.8 cm

b
12 cm

Density = 12.84 g/cm³

42 cm

18.5 cm

11 A cuboid's length is 10 cm and its breadth is 6 cm. The density of the cuboid is 2.5 g/cm³. Given that the cuboid's mass is 900 g, find its height.

12 A solid cone has radius 6.8 cm and slant height 17.4 cm. Given that it has a mass of 1.2 kg decide if it will float in water. The density of water is 1 g/cm³.

13 A cylinder's height is 8 cm. The density of the cylinder is 1.6 g/cm³. Given that the cylinder's mass is 540 g, find its diameter to 2 decimal places.

This chapter is about

- understanding the continuous nature of measure
- understanding that measurements given are only approximate to the degree of accuracy used in recording them
- knowing what is meant by the upper and lower bounds
- calculating the maximum and minimum values of expressions given the measurements and their accuracy.

1 Copy and complete the table below.

	Measurement	Accuracy	Lower bound	Upper bound
1	15 cm	nearest cm		
2	5.9 cm	nearest mm		
3	200 cm	nearest 10 cm		
4	23.80 sec	nearest hundredth of a second		
5	464 ml	nearest ml		
6	$5.5\,m^2$	1 decimal place		
7	75.0 cm	1 decimal place		
8	6000 g	Nearest 100 g		

2 Find the maximum value for the sum of each pair of measurements.
   a 43.2 cm and 81.7 cm (both to the nearest millimetre)
   b 10.31 seconds and 19.17 seconds (both to the nearest hundredth of a second)

3 Find the minimum value for the sum of each pair of measurements in question **2**.

4 Find the maximum value for the difference between each of these pairs of measurements.
   a 489 m and 526 m (both to the nearest metre)
   b 0.728 kg and 1.026 kg (both to the nearest gram)

5 Find the minimum value for the difference between each pair of measurements in question **4**.

6 Find the greatest and least value for the sum of the times 3 hours 23 minutes and 1 hour 37 minutes, each correct to the nearest minute.

7 A length of timber measures 240 mm, correct to the nearest millimetre. Paul cuts off a piece from one end. He intends it to be 90 mm long but his cut is only accurate to the nearest centimetre. Give the greatest and least value of the length of the piece that is left.

8 One day the high tide was 2.3 m above a mark on the harbour wall. The low tide on the same day was 2.0 m below the mark. Both measurements were correct to 1 decimal place. Calculate, in metres, the least value for the difference between the high and low tides.

9 Two parcels weigh 247 g and 252 g, each correct to the nearest gram. The cost of posting parcels increases for those weighing 500 g or more. If these two parcels are fastened together, will they certainly weigh less than 500 g? Explain your answer.

10 Find the greatest value for the area of the floor of rectangular rooms with these dimensions.
   a 4.3 m by 6.2 m (both to 2 significant figures)
   b 4.27 m by 6.24 m (both to the nearest centimetre)

11 Find the least value for the area of the floor of each room in question **10**.

12 Calculate the greatest value for the average speed in each of these situations.
   Give your answers to 4 significant figures.
   a 157 km (to the nearest kilometre) in 2.5 hours (to the nearest 0.1 hour)
   b 800.0 cm (to the nearest mm) in 103.47 seconds (to the nearest hundredth of a second)

13 Find the least value for the average speed in each situation in question **12**.

14 Calculate the minimum and maximum widths of these rectangles.
   a Area 400 cm² (to the nearest cm²), length 15 cm (to the nearest cm)
   b Area 24.5 cm² (to 3 significant figures), length 5.7 cm (to 2 significant figures)

15 Calculate the maximum and minimum heights of these cuboids.
   a Volume 400 cm³ (to the nearest cm³), length 10 cm, width 5 cm (both to the nearest cm)
   b Volume 50.0 m³ (to 3 significant figures), length 5.0 m, width 2.8 m (both to 2 significant figures)

16 Niall has eight rods, each of length 10 cm, correct to the nearest centimetre.
   He places them in the shape of a rectangle as in the diagram.

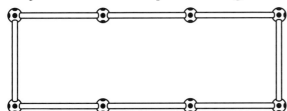

   a What is the minimum length of the rectangle?
   b Calculate the maximum area of the rectangle.

17 The length of Edward's training run is 380 m, correct to the nearest 10 m. Edward completes his run at an average speed of 3.9 m/s, correct to 1 decimal place.
   Calculate the greatest possible time Edward takes to complete his run.

18 P and Q are measured as 6.3 and 9.4, each correct to 1 decimal place.
   a Find the maximum value of
      i $P + Q$ **ii** PQ **iii** $\dfrac{Q}{P}$.
   b Find the minimum value of
      i $Q - P$ **ii** Q^2 **iii** $\sqrt{P}$.

19 K is measured as 420 to the nearest 10. M is measured as 800 to the nearest 100.
   a Find the maximum value of
      i $3K$ **ii** $M - K$ **iii** $\dfrac{M}{K}$.
   b Find the minimum value of
      i M^2 **ii** $M + K$ **iii** $\sqrt{K}$.

20 C, D and E are measured as 2.64, 1.82 and 4.07, each correct to 3 significant figures.
   a Find the maximum value of $E - C + D$.   **b** Find the minimum value of $\dfrac{3E - 2D}{C}$.

This chapter is about

- knowing the properties of a reflection, rotation, translation and an enlargement
- drawing the image of a shape after each of these transformations
- finding the original shape given the image and the transformation
- describing fully the transformation given the original shape and its image
- finding the image after two transformations.

Exercise A

1 Copy the diagram.

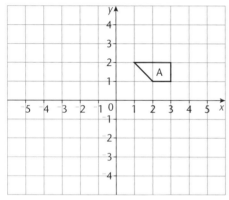

   a Reflect trapezium A in the x-axis. Label the image B.
   b Reflect trapezium A in the line $y = 1$. Label the image C.
   c Reflect trapezium A in the y-axis. Label the image D.
   d Reflect trapezium A in the line $x = 3$. Label the image E.

2 Draw a pair of axes and label them -3 to 3 for x and y.
   a Draw a triangle with vertices at $(-1, 1)$, $(-1, 3)$ and $(-2, 3)$. Label it A.
   b Reflect triangle A in the line $x = \dfrac{1}{2}$. Label the image B.
   c Reflect triangle A in the line $y = x$. Label the image C.
   d Reflect triangle A in the line $y = -x$. Label the image D.

3 Look at this diagram.

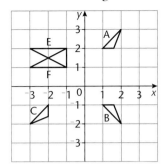

Describe fully the single transformation that maps
a Triangle A on to triangle B
b Triangle A on to triangle C
c Triangle E on to triangle F.

4 Look at this diagram.

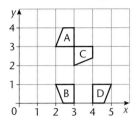

Describe fully 3 different reflections in the diagram.

5 Copy the diagram.

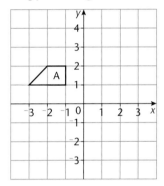

a Rotate trapezium A through 180° about the origin. Label the image B.
b Rotate trapezium A through 90° clockwise about the point (0, 1). Label the image C.
c Rotate trapezium A through 90° anticlockwise about the point (−1, 1). Label the image D.

6 Copy the diagram.

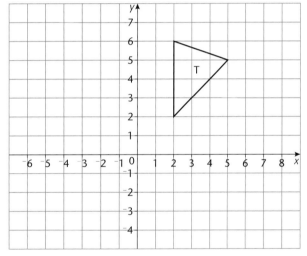

a Rotate triangle T through 90° anticlockwise about the point (5, 5). Label the image A.
b Describe fully the transformation that maps triangle A on to triangle T.
c On the same diagram, rotate triangle T through 180° about the point (0, 3). Label the image B.
d Describe fully the transformation that maps triangle B on to triangle T.

7 Look at this diagram.

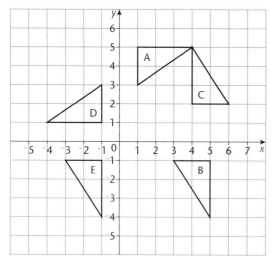

Describe fully the single transformation that maps

a A on to B   **b** A on to C
c A on to D   **d** D on to E.

8 Look at the diagram.

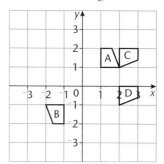

Describe fully the single transformation that maps

a Trapezium A on to trapezium B
b Trapezium A on to trapezium C
c Trapezium A on to trapezium D.

9 Copy the diagram.

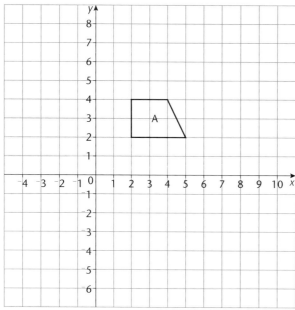

a Translate shape A by $\begin{pmatrix} 0 \\ -6 \end{pmatrix}$. Label the image B.

b Translate shape A by $\begin{pmatrix} 4 \\ 3 \end{pmatrix}$. Label the image C.

c Translate shape A by $\begin{pmatrix} -6 \\ 4 \end{pmatrix}$. Label the image D.

d Translate shape A by $\begin{pmatrix} -4 \\ -7 \end{pmatrix}$. Label the image E.

10 Draw a pair of axes and label them −3 to 5 for x and y. Draw a triangle with vertices at (2, 1), (2, 3) and (3, 1). Label it A.

a Translate triangle A by $\begin{pmatrix} 2 \\ 1 \end{pmatrix}$. Label the image B.

b Translate triangle A by $\begin{pmatrix} -5 \\ -3 \end{pmatrix}$. Label the image C.

c Translate triangle A by $\begin{pmatrix} 2 \\ -4 \end{pmatrix}$. Label the image D.

11 Look at this diagram.

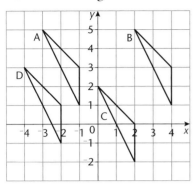

Describe fully the single transformation that maps
a Triangle A on to triangle B
b Triangle A on to triangle C
c Triangle A on to triangle D
d Triangle B on to triangle D.

Exercise B

1 Draw a pair of axes and label them 0 to 7 for both x and y.
a Draw a trapezium with vertices at (1, 2), (1, 3), (2, 3) and (3, 2). Label it A.
b Enlarge trapezium A by scale factor 3, with centre of enlargement (1, 2). Label the image B.
c Describe fully the single transformation that maps trapezium B on to trapezium A.

2 Draw a pair of axes and label them 0 to 6 for both x and y.
a Draw a triangle with vertices at (0, 6), (3, 6) and (3, 3). Label it A.
b Enlarge triangle A by scale factor $\frac{1}{3}$, with the origin as the centre of enlargement. Label it B.
c Describe fully the single transformation that maps triangle B on to triangle A.

3 Draw a pair of axes and label them 0 to 8 for both x and y.
a Draw a triangle with vertices at (2, 1), (2, 3) and (3, 2). Label it A.
b Enlarge triangle A by scale factor $2\frac{1}{2}$, with the origin as the centre of enlargement. Label it B.
c Describe fully the single transformation that maps triangle B on to triangle A.

4 Look at this diagram.

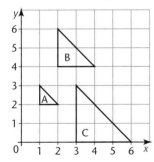

Describe fully the single transformation that maps
a Triangle A on to triangle B
b Triangle B on to triangle A
c Triangle A on to triangle C
d Triangle C on to triangle A.

5 Draw a set of axes. Label the x-axis and the y-axis from −7 to 6.
Plot the points (1, 2), (1, 3) and (3, 3) and join them to form a triangle.
Enlarge the triangle with scale factor of −2 and centre of enlargement (0, 0).

6 Draw a set of axes with both the x-axis and y-axis from −10 to 6.
Plot the points A(2, 2), B(4, 2) and C(2, 4) and join them to form a triangle.
Enlarge triangle ABC by a scale factor of −3 using the point (1, 1) as the centre of enlargement.

7 Look at this diagram.

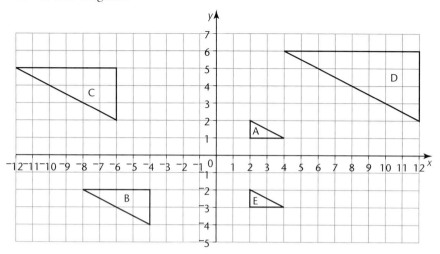

Describe fully the single transformation that maps
a Triangle A on to triangle B
b Triangle A on to triangle C
c Triangle A on to triangle D
d Triangle C on to triangle E
e Triangle B on to triangle E
f Triangle C on to triangle A.

Exercise C

1 Look at the diagram.

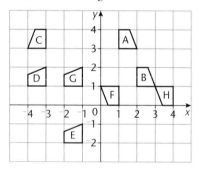

Describe fully the single transformation that maps
a Shape A on to shape B
b Shape A on to shape C
c Shape A on to shape D
d Shape D on to shape E
e Shape A on to shape F
f Shape E on to shape G
g Shape B on to shape H
h Shape H on to shape F.

2 Look at the diagram.

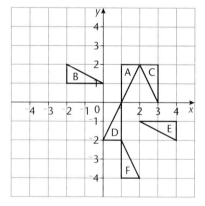

Describe fully the single transformation that maps
a Triangle A on to triangle B
b Triangle A on to triangle C
c Triangle A on to triangle D
d Triangle A on to triangle E
e Triangle A on to triangle F

3 Draw a set of axes. Label the x-axis from 0 to 10 and the y-axis from −3 to 5.
Plot the points (1, 2), (1, 4) and (4, 4) and join them to form a triangle. Label it A.
   a Reflect triangle A in the line $x = 5$. Label the image B.
   b On the same grid, reflect triangle B in the line $y = 1$. Label the image C.
   c Describe fully the single transformation that is equivalent to a reflection in the line $x = 5$
   followed by a reflection in the line $y = 1$.

4 Draw a set of axes. Label the x-axis from 0 to 9 and the y-axis from −4 to 4.
Plot the points (1, 3), (3, 3) and (3, 2) and join them to form a triangle. Label it D.
   a Rotate triangle D through 90° clockwise about the point (0, 0).Label the image E.
   b On the same grid, rotate triangle E through 180° about the point (5, −2). Label the image F.
   c Describe fully the single transformation that is equivalent to a rotation through 90°
   clockwise about the point (0, 0) followed by a rotation through 180° about the point (5, −2).

5 Draw a set of axes. Label the x-axis from −5 to 5 and the y-axis from 0 to 6.
Plot the points (−3, 1), (0, 1) and (−2, 3) and join them to form a triangle. Label it A.
   a Translate triangle A by the vector $\begin{pmatrix} 4 \\ 0 \end{pmatrix}$. Label the image B.
   b Translate triangle B by the vector $\begin{pmatrix} -3 \\ 2 \end{pmatrix}$. Label the image C.
   c Describe fully the single transformation that is equivalent to a translation by the vector $\begin{pmatrix} 4 \\ 0 \end{pmatrix}$
   followed by a translation by the vector $\begin{pmatrix} -3 \\ 2 \end{pmatrix}$.

6 Draw a set of axes. Label the x-axis and the y-axis from −6 to 6.
Plot the points (1, 1), (2, 1) and (1, 3) and join them to form a triangle. Label it D.
   a Enlarge triangle D with scale factor 2 and centre of enlargement (0, 0). Label the image E.
   b Rotate triangle E through 180° and centre of rotation (0, 0). Label the image F.
   c Describe fully the single transformation that is equivalent to an enlargement with scale
   factor 2 and centre (0, 0) followed by a rotation through 180° and centre (0, 0).

7 Draw a set of axes. Draw a triangle with vertices at (1, 1) (1, 2) and (4, 2). Label it A.
Draw the image of A after a reflection in the line $y = -x$ followed by a rotation through 90°
anticlockwise about (0, −1). Label the image B.

8 Shape P is reflected in the line $x = 4$ and then translated $\begin{pmatrix} 5 \\ -2 \end{pmatrix}$ to give shape Q. Describe the
two transformations that will map Q back to P.

9 What is the inverse of these transformations?
   a Rotation 90° clockwise about (1, −5) followed by translation $\begin{pmatrix} -4 \\ 7 \end{pmatrix}$.
   b Enlargement scale factor 3.5 about centre (−2, 3).
   c Rotation 90° anticlockwise about (−3, 0) followed by reflection in $y = x$.
   d Translation $\begin{pmatrix} 6 \\ 2 \end{pmatrix}$ followed by translation $\begin{pmatrix} -2 \\ 3 \end{pmatrix}$.
   e Reflection in $y = 3$ followed by translation $\begin{pmatrix} -7 \\ 4 \end{pmatrix}$.

This chapter is about

- understanding and knowing how to use the handling data cycle
- designing a recording sheet
- designing a questionnaire
- saying why questions are unsuitable
- suggesting alternative questions
- designing a questionnaire to test a hypothesis.

1   Design a recording sheet to investigate the main food eaten for breakfast by Year 11 pupils.

2   Marge is designing a questionnaire to find out opinions on a new supermarket being built on the edge of town. Here is one of her questions.

Do you not agree that a new supermarket on the edge of town will be harmful to our town centre?

Yes ☐   No ☐

   a Name one thing wrong with the question.
   b Name one thing wrong with the response section.

3   Ned is designing a questionnaire to find out the eating habits of people in his community. One of his questions is:
How often do you eat fruit and vegetables?

   1–4 times ☐   4–8 times ☐   8–12 times ☐   More than 12 times ☐

   a Name one thing wrong with his question.
   b Name two things wrong with the response section.

4   Lucy wants to survey the teachers in her school for her Health and Social Care project. One of her questions is:
How old are you?

   a Name one thing wrong with this question.
   b Write a more suitable question and response section in order to gather the information that Lucy requires.

5   Rhiannon wants to know what activities people will want to do while on holiday at her family's caravan park. She asks this question:
What activities do you like to do?

   Tennis ☐   Swimming ☐   Crazy golf ☐   Football ☐

   a Name one thing wrong with her question.
   b Name two things wrong with her response section.
   c Rewrite the question and add a more suitable response section.

6 You wish to investigate how regularly students at your school visit the cinema.
You decide to write a questionnaire to find out.
Write down two useful questions which would help you gather the necessary information.

7 A local radio station is about to start broadcasting.
They decide to send out a questionnaire to find out the sort of programmes that are preferred.
Comment on each of these questions and where necessary write a more suitable one with response section.

  a What type of programme do you like most?
  b Do you listen to the radio in the afternoon?
  c Do you like competitions and phone-ins?
  d How much do you earn?
Are there any other questions that you think will be useful for the radio station?

8 Design a questionnaire to test each hypothesis. Include two suitable questions and their response sections.

  a Children who live in the countryside go to the play park less than children who live in the town.
  b Pupils who text more on their mobile phones do not perform as well in exams compared to those who text less.
  c People who eat carrots have better eyesight than people who do not eat carrots.
  d People who are musical are also good at Maths.

CHAPTER 43

Statistical diagrams

This chapter is about

- understanding what is meant by frequency
- distinguishing between continuous and discrete data
- constructing a frequency distribution table
- drawing and interpreting frequency diagrams
- drawing and interpreting frequency polygons
- drawing and interpreting stem and leaf diagrams
- drawing and using scatter graphs
- knowing and recognising the three types of correlation
- using flow diagrams.

Exercise A

1 These are the marks of 30 students in a test.

32	42	23	37	28
12	37	6	5	37
17	18	31	29	27
11	21	37	28	37
22	31	23	47	23
12	24	34	41	43

a Draw a grouped frequency table for the data. Use groups 0–9, 10–19, etc.

b Draw a frequency diagram.

2 As part of a survey, Eve measured the heights, in centimetres, of the 50 teachers in her school. Here are her results.

168	194	156	167	177
180	188	172	170	169
174	178	186	174	166
165	159	173	185	162
163	174	180	184	173
182	161	176	170	169
178	175	172	179	173
162	177	176	184	191
181	165	163	185	178
175	182	164	179	168

a Draw a grouped frequency table for the data. Use groups $155 \leqslant h < 160$, $160 \leqslant h < 165$, etc.

b Draw a frequency diagram.

3 This frequency diagram shows the times taken by a group of girls to run a race.

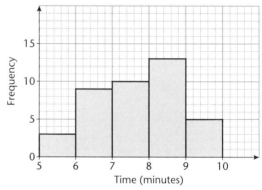

a What is the modal class interval?

b How many girls took part in the race?

c What percentage of the girls took less than 7 minutes?

d Work out an estimate for the mean time.

4 This table shows the heights of 40 plants.

Height (h cm)	Frequency
$3 \leqslant h < 4$	1
$4 \leqslant h < 5$	7
$5 \leqslant h < 6$	10
$6 \leqslant h < 7$	12
$7 \leqslant h < 8$	8
$8 \leqslant h < 9$	2

Draw a frequency polygon to show this data.

5 This table shows the times taken for a group of children to get from home to school.

Time (minutes)	Frequency
$0 < t \leqslant 5$	3
$5 < t \leqslant 10$	15
$10 < t \leqslant 15$	27
$15 < t \leqslant 20$	34
$20 < t \leqslant 25$	19
$25 < t \leqslant 30$	2

Draw a frequency polygon to show this data.

6 The table below shows the frequency distribution for the vital lung capacities of pupils in Year 12.

Vital lung capacity (litres)	Frequency girls	Frequency boys
$3.4 \leqslant x < 3.6$	3	2
$3.6 \leqslant x < 3.8$	7	5
$3.8 \leqslant x < 4.0$	26	24
$4.0 \leqslant x < 4.2$	17	25
$4.2 \leqslant x < 4.4$	4	7
$4.4 \leqslant x < 4.6$	1	3

a Draw a frequency polygon to show the information for the Year 12 boys.
b On the same axes draw a frequency polygon to show the information for the Year 12 girls.
c How many pupils are in Year 12?
d Using the frequency polygons, write down one comparison between the boys' and girls' vital lung capacities.

7 These are the test results for 30 pupils who sat a Geography test.

29 39 46 17 21 30 43 47 39 31
18 32 45 50 41 32 37 39 22 14
28 39 40 47 38 31 25 29 35 42

a Draw a stem and leaf diagram to show these results.
b Use your diagram to find
i the median
ii the mode
iii the range.

8 The ages of the first 25 men and the first 25 women to enter a supermarket on a Wednesday were recorded.

Men

52 62 73 37 69 62 77 76 65 47
47 48 61 39 27 51 21 47 58 57
61 74 82 81 64

Women

62 61 63 37 23 52 44 64 51 53
52 42 33 77 49 41 84 82 71 64
40 67 61 52 54

a Draw a back-to-back stem and leaf diagram to show the ages of men and women.
b What is the difference between the median age for the men and the median age for the women?

9 Use the stem and leaf diagram below to answer the questions that follow.

```
3 |  4  5  8  9              Key 3 | 8 = 3.8 cm
4 |  0  2  3  6  8  8
5 |  1  3  3  5  6  7  9
6 |  4  6  8
7 |  0  2
```

a Find the range. **b** Find the median.
c Find the mean. **d** How many values are less than 2 inches?

10 The stem and leaf diagram shows the results for the boys and girls from 11T in a recent Maths test.

Boys		Girls

```
          5 | 0 | 1  6
      9 9 3 3 | 1 | 2  2  7  8
    8 7 6 6 4 | 2 | 0  5  6  6  7
    9 9 9 6 5 | 3 | 1  2  4  5
          2 1 | 4 |
```

Key 3 | 1 = 31%

From the stem and leaf diagram find

a The median score for the boys   **b** The range for the girls
c The number of pupils in class 11T   **d** The range for the class
e The mode for the boys   **f** The mode for the class.

Exercise B

1 For each of the graphs below, describe the correlation.

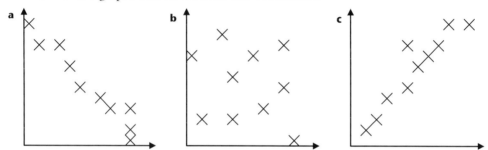

2 This table gives the average maximum temperature and the average rainfall in June for 10 different cities.

Temperature (°C)	18	19	20	21	22	23	24	27	28	29
Rainfall (mm)	47	64	60	73	84	37	49	29	63	47

a Draw a scatter diagram to show this information.
b Comment on the relationship, if any, between the temperature and the rainfall.
c Another city has an average maximum temperature of 23 °C in June.
What can you deduce from the scatter diagram about the average rainfall in this city?

3 Bill grows tomatoes. As an experiment he divided his land into eight plots.
He used a different amount of fertiliser on each plot.
The table shows the weight of tomatoes he got from each of the plots.

Amount of fertiliser (g/m²)	10	20	30	40	50	60	70	80
Weight of tomatoes (kg)	36	41	58	60	70	76	75	92

a Draw a scatter diagram to show this information.
b Describe the correlation shown in the scatter diagram.
c Draw a line of best fit on your scatter diagram.
d What weight of tomatoes should Bill expect to get if he uses 75 g/m² of fertiliser?

4 The table shows the prices and mileages of seven second-hand cars of the same model.

Price (£)	6000	3500	1000	8500	5500	3500	6000
Mileage	27 000	69 000	92 000	17 000	53 000	82 000	43 000

a Draw a scatter diagram to show this information.
b Describe the correlation shown in the scatter diagram.
c Draw a line of best fit on your scatter diagram.
d Use your line of best fit to estimate
  i   the price of a car of this model which has covered 18 000 miles
  ii the mileage of a car of this model which costs £4000.

Exercise C

Look at the flow diagrams and follow the instructions until you get the answer.

1 Start with $x = 4$ and $y = 8$.

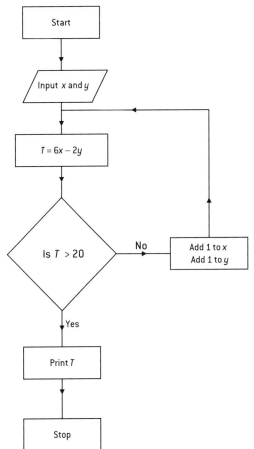

2 Start with $A = 3$ and $B = 2$.

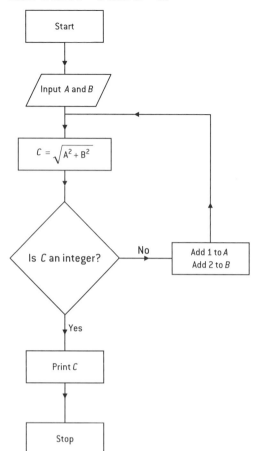

3 Start with $m = 0$ and $n = 3$.

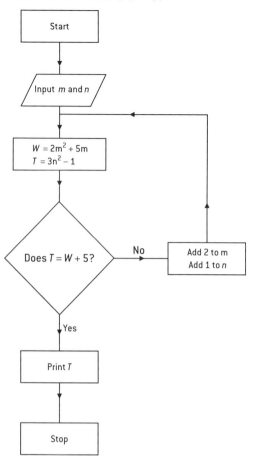

CHAPTER 44

Statistical averages and spread

This chapter is about

- defining and distinguishing between mode, median and mean
- understanding what is meant by the range
- calculating the range, mode, median and mean of a frequency distribution
- finding the limits of the median and modal class of a grouped frequency distribution
- calculating an estimate for the mean of a grouped frequency distribution
- using means in problems
- comparing distributions
- choosing the most appropriate statistical average.

Exercise A

In questions **1** to **4**
    a find the mode   **b** find the range   **c** calculate the mean   **d** find the median.

1

Number	Frequency
1	3
2	2
3	4
4	5
5	7
6	2
7	0
8	1
9	0
10	1

2

Number of drawing pins in a box	Number of boxes
98	5
99	14
100	36
101	28
102	17
103	13
104	7

3

Number of snacks per day	Frequency
0	23
1	68
2	39
3	21
4	10
5	3
6	1

4

Number of letters received on Monday	Frequency
0	19
1	37
2	18
3	24
4	12
5	5
6	2
7	3

5 The table shows the numbers of trains arriving late at a station in the month of May.

Number of trains arriving late each day	Frequency
0–4	18
5–9	9
10–14	3
15–19	0
20–24	1

a Write down the modal class.
b In which class does the median lie?
c Calculate an estimate of the mean.

6 The table shows the numbers of days the students in Year 11 were absent last year.

Number of days' absence	Frequency
0–3	13
4–7	18
8–11	9
12–15	4
16–19	0
20–23	1
24–27	3

a Write down the modal class.
b In which class does the median lie?
c Calculate an estimate of the mean.

7 The table shows the heights of sunflowers in centimetres.

Height of sunflower in centimetres (x)	Frequency
$100 \leqslant x < 110$	6
$110 \leqslant x < 120$	13
$120 \leqslant x < 130$	35
$130 \leqslant x < 140$	29
$140 \leqslant x < 150$	16
$150 \leqslant x < 160$	11

a Write down the modal class.
b In which class does the median lie?
c Calculate an estimate of the mean.

8 The table shows the times taken to complete a race in minutes.

Time to complete race in minutes (x)	Frequency
$54 \leqslant x < 56$	1
$56 \leqslant x < 58$	4
$58 \leqslant x < 60$	11
$60 \leqslant x < 62$	6
$62 \leqslant x < 64$	2
$64 \leqslant x < 66$	1

a Write down the modal group.
b In which group does the median lie?
c Calculate an estimate of the mean.

9 The table shows the heights of shrubs in metres.

Height of shrub in metres (x)	Frequency
$0.3 \leqslant x < 0.6$	57
$0.6 \leqslant x < 0.9$	41
$0.9 \leqslant x < 1.2$	36
$1.2 \leqslant x < 1.5$	24
$1.5 \leqslant x < 1.8$	15

a Write down the modal group.
b In which group does the median lie?
c Calculate an estimate of the mean.
d Given that measurements are taken to the nearest 10 cm, what is the height of the shortest possible shrub?

Exercise B

1 The frequency table shows the number of pets owned by pupils in Year 9.

Number of pets	Frequency
1	9
2	5
3	2
4	x
5	1

Given that the mean number of pets was 2.1, calculate the number of pupils who own four pets.

2 David rolled a dice a number of times and calculated the mean to be 3.2.

Number on dice	1	2	3	4	5	6
Frequency	10	5	10	4	4	

The number of times he rolled a six is missing from the table. Work out how many times he rolled a six.

3 The frequency table shows the number of siblings that pupils in Year 11 have.

Number of siblings	Frequency
0	5
1	10
2	x
3	4
4	2

Given that the mean number of siblings is 1.75, calculate the number of pupils who have two siblings.

4 An estimate for the mean height is 161 cm. Find n.

Height of pupil (cm)	Frequency
$140 < h \leqslant 150$	8
$150 < h \leqslant 160$	17
$160 < h \leqslant 170$	15
$170 < h \leqslant 180$	n
$180 < h \leqslant 190$	3

5 The mean height of 5 pupils is 149 cm. A sixth pupil is measured and has a height of 161 cm. Calculate the mean height of all six pupils.

6 Mr Black recorded the mean test score of the 25 pupils in his class as 72%. He then realised that the lowest score was 50%, not 60%. What is the actual mean test score for his class?

7 In a class of 25 pupils the mean for a Maths test is 64%. In a second class of 20 pupils the mean for the same test is 55%. Find the mean for both classes.

8 The mean contents of a sample of 50 packets of crisps is 35.4 grams. The mean contents of a sample of 30 different packets of crisps is 34.6 grams. Find the mean of all the packets sampled.

9 The mean pocket money for the 14 boys in a class is £1.74. The mean pocket money for the 10 girls in the same class is £1.88. Find the mean pocket money for the whole class.

10 Matt has x marbles. Daniel had 3 more than Matt and Beth has 6 less than Matt. The mean number of marbles is 6. Form an equation and solve it to find the number of marbles that Matt has.

11 Tim and Zoe grow potatoes. They each dig up 10 potatoes and weigh them.
Here are their results, in grams.

Tim	Zoe
190	230
170	210
180	270
120	90
160	210
100	180
320	260
210	270
220	110
270	250

Use suitable calculations to compare their results. Give reasons for your decisions.

12 Two friends Aoife and Clare in Year 11 record the number of homeworks they receive **each week** from their subject teachers for a whole year.

Homeworks set (Aoife)	Frequency	Homeworks set (Clare)	Frequency
0–1	2	0–1	0
2–3	3	2–3	0
4–5	5	4–5	3
6–7	8	6–7	8
8–9	9	8–9	13
10–11	9	10–11	11
12–13	2	12–13	4
14–15	1	14–15	0

Use suitable calculations to compare their results.

13 The lengths of 200 leaves from a variety of trees were measured at each of two sites, one exposed and one sheltered.
The results are shown in the table.

Length of leaf (*l* cm)	Frequency	
	Exposed site	Sheltered site
$7 < l \leqslant 8$	8	0
$8 < l \leqslant 9$	25	2
$9 < l \leqslant 10$	62	14
$10 < l \leqslant 11$	53	31
$11 < l \leqslant 12$	32	88
$12 < l \leqslant 13$	17	42
$13 < l \leqslant 14$	2	18
$14 < l \leqslant 15$	1	5

Make three comparisons between the leaves taken from the two sites.

14 The following amounts are the salaries of a sample of 10 employees at a large factory.

£17300   £15690   £21650   £12480   £47340   £17000   £72600   £14550   £18890   £28750
  a Calculate the mean salary for this sample.
  b Calculate the median salary for the sample.
  c Which average is more appropriate?

15 State the most appropriate statistical average to use in each of these. Give a reason for your answer.
  a A shop owner ordering in men's trousers for the autumn and winter season.
  b A teacher wants to find the average height of pupils in Year 10.
  c A scientist wants to find the number of bacteria in a sample of 12 colonies.
  d A writer wants to know the average number of words per page.
  e A farmer wants to know the average amount of fuel used each month.
  f An electronics shop is wanting to order in different makes of mobile phone.
  g A shopkeeper wants to work out the average takings for a month.
  h A café owner wants to order in fillings for sandwiches.

CHAPTER 45

Cumulative frequency curves and box plots

This chapter is about

- defining and using limits and boundaries
- knowing what is meant by quartiles
- finding quartiles and inter quartile range
- drawing and interpreting cumulative frequency curves
- drawing and interpreting box plots.

Exercise A

1 The cumulative frequency diagram represents the heights of trees in a park.

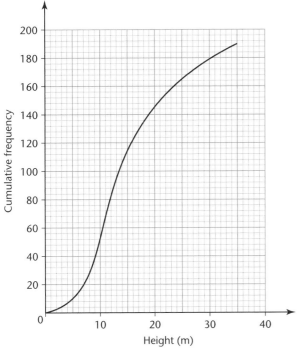

a How many trees are there in the park?
b How many trees have a height of less than 12 m?
c What percentage of the trees have a height more than 26 m?

2 The frequency table shows information about the masses of 100 letters.

Mass(m grams)	Frequency
$30 < m \leqslant 40$	7
$40 < m \leqslant 50$	12
$50 < m \leqslant 60$	24
$60 < m \leqslant 70$	32
$70 < m \leqslant 80$	18
$80 < m \leqslant 90$	5
$90 < m \leqslant 100$	2

a Copy and complete the cumulative frequency table.

Mass(m grams)	Cumulative frequency
$m \leqslant 40$	7
$m \leqslant 50$	19
$m \leqslant 60$	
$m \leqslant 70$	
$m \leqslant 80$	
$m \leqslant 90$	
$m \leqslant 100$	

b Draw a cumulative frequency diagram.
c Use your diagram to find the median and the interquartile range of these masses.

3 The heights of 150 plants were measured. The results are shown in the table.

Height (h cm)	Frequency
$0 < h \leqslant 10$	15
$10 < h \leqslant 20$	23
$20 < h \leqslant 30$	36
$30 < h \leqslant 40$	42
$40 < h \leqslant 50$	24
$50 < h \leqslant 60$	10

a Draw a cumulative frequency table and diagram for these heights.
b Find the median and the interquartile range of the heights.
c Use your cumulative frequency diagram to estimate the number of plants over 37 cm in height.

Exercise B

1   The graph below shows the cumulative frequency of marks obtained in a theory test.

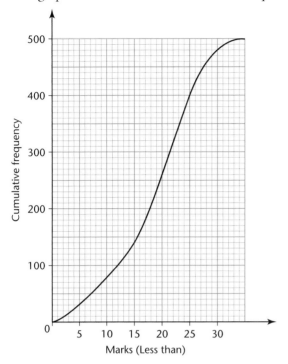

Marks (Less than)

Use the graph to estimate
a   The upper quartile
b   The median
c   The inter quartile range
d   How many obtained more than 10 marks
e   How many obtained between 20 and 30 marks.

2   The graph below shows the cumulative frequency of times taken by pupils to complete an assignment.

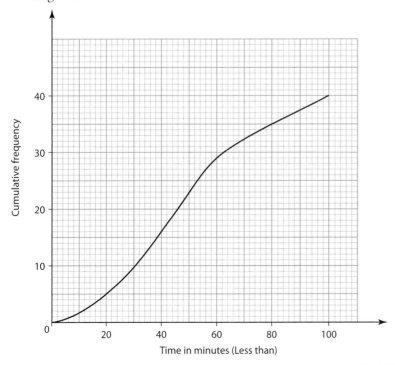

Time in minutes (Less than)

Use the graph to estimate
a   The median
b   The inter quartile range
c   How many took less than 20 minutes
d   How many took between 30 and 60 minutes
e   How many took between 80 and 100 minutes.

Exercise C

1 Draw a box plot to show this data.
Minimum = 2
Maximum = 14
Median = 9
Lower quartile = 5
Upper quartile = 11

2 Draw a box plot to show this data.
Minimum = 5
Median = 10
Lower quartile = 8
Upper quartile = 11
Range = 12

3 Draw a box plot to show this data.
Minimum = 21
Maximum = 32
Median = 26
Upper quartile = 30
Interquartile range = 6

4 Draw a box plot to show this data.
Maximum = 44
Median = 35
Lower quartile = 33
Range = 14
Interquartile range = 9

5 Draw a box plot to show this data.
2, 3, 7, 7, 10, 11, 15, 15, 16

6 Draw a box plot to show this data.
17, 6, 9, 10, 11, 16, 4, 4, 7, 15

Exercise D

1   The box plots show the distribution of the weekly wages of men and women who work at a factory.

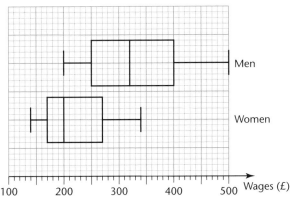

a   For the men, write down
   i   the median
   ii the range
   iii the interquartile range.
b   For the women, write down
   i   the median
   ii the range
   iii the interquartile range.
c   Make two comparisons between the weekly wages of men and women at this factory.

2   The box plots represent the times, in minutes, spent making mobile phone calls by a sample of 50 boys and 50 girls in one week.

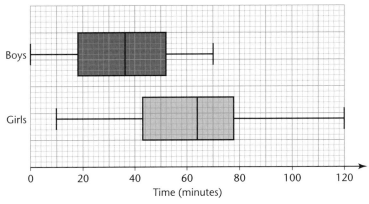

Make two comparisons of the times spent making mobile phone calls by the boys and the girls, stating which statistics you use.

3   These marks were obtained by two students in 12 tests.

| **Alice** | 6 | 7 | 9 | 9 | 10 | 13 | 18 | 20 | 21 | 21 | 22 | 24 |
| **Ronnie** | 3 | 11 | 12 | 13 | 14 | 14 | 16 | 16 | 17 | 17 | 18 | 28 |

a   Draw a box plot for Alice's marks.
b   Draw a box plot for Ronnie's marks.
c   Make two comparisons of the two sets of marks.

4 The cumulative frequency graph shows the heights of 200 girls and 200 boys.

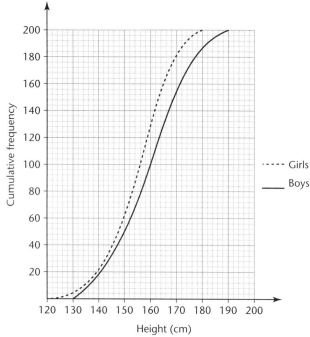

a Use the graph to find for the girls:
  i the median
  ii the interquartile range
  iii the range.
b Use the graph to find for the boys:
  i the median
  ii the interquartile range
  iii the range.
c Make two comparisons of the heights of the girls and the heights of the boys.
d i Draw a box plot for the girls.
  ii Draw a box plot for the boys.

5 The table shows the mean and interquartile range of Kevin and Dermot in their last twenty 400 m races.

	Mean	Interquartile range
Kevin	45.2 seconds	4.7 seconds
Dermot	46.1 seconds	2.1 seconds

Which runner would you select for the team? Give your reasons.

6 The table shows the mean and the interquartile range of the lifetime of two makes of battery.

	Mean	Interquartile range
Make A	23.4 hours	10.6 hours
Make B	19.3 hours	1.7 hours

Which battery would you purchase in each of these cases?
a You need a single battery. Give your reasons.
b You are a buyer for a company which uses 50 batteries a week. Give your reasons.

CHAPTER 46

Histograms and sampling

This chapter is about

- drawing histograms
- interpreting histograms
- understanding population and sample
- understanding bias
- knowing the different sampling methods
- using stratified random sampling.

Exercise A

1 The table summarises the distribution of the heights of 120 children.

Height(h cm)	Number of children
$75 < h \leqslant 100$	15
$100 < h \leqslant 120$	20
$120 < h \leqslant 140$	32
$140 < h \leqslant 160$	44
$160 < h \leqslant 180$	9

Draw a histogram to show this information.

2 The table summarises the distribution of the money raised for charity by runners in a sponsored race.

Amount raised ($£x$)	Frequency
$0 < x \leqslant 50$	6
$50 < x \leqslant 100$	22
$100 < x \leqslant 200$	31
$200 < x \leqslant 500$	42
$5000 < x \leqslant 1000$	15

Draw a histogram to show this information.

3 The table summarises how much the workers at a factory earn each week.

Amount earned (£)	Frequency
$0 < x \leqslant 250$	25
$250 < x \leqslant 400$	30
$400 < x \leqslant 450$	55
$450 < x \leqslant 500$	30
$500 < x \leqslant 1000$	80

Draw a histogram to show this information.

4 This histogram shows the distribution of time spent watching TV in a week by a group of people.

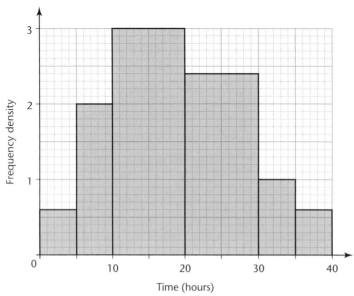

Time (hours)

a How many people watched TV for 5 to 10 hours?
b How many people watched TV for more than 15 hours?
c How many people watched TV for less than 35 hours?

5 The histogram shows the distribution of money raised in a sponsored race.

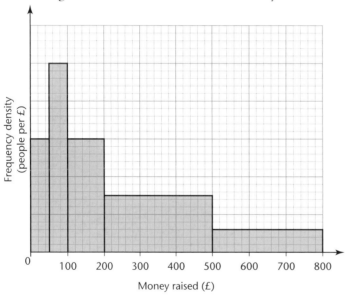

Money raised (£)

Fifteen people raised £50 or less.

a Copy and complete the frequency table for this data.

Money raised (£)	Frequency
$0 < m \leqslant 50$	15
$50 < m \leqslant 100$	

b Calculate an estimate of the mean amount of money raised.

6 This histogram represents a distribution of waiting times in an outpatients department one day.

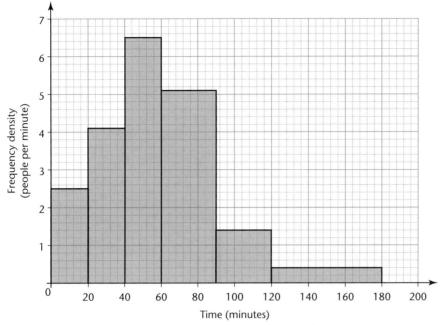

a Work out how many people waited more than 2 hours.
b Work out how many people waited less than 1 hour.
c Calculate an estimate of the mean waiting time.

7 The two histograms show the ages of the passengers on two buses one morning.

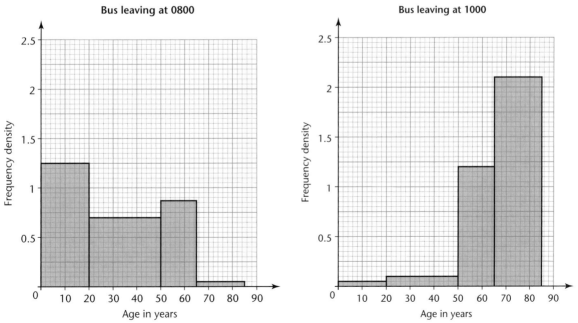

Write down two comparisons of the histograms.

Exercise B

1 You need to obtain a representative sample of 1000 people for an investigation into how often people eat out at restaurants.
   Comment on the following methods for obtaining the sample.
   a By choosing 1000 names from the telephone directory.
   b By stopping 1000 people at random outside the railway station.
   c By asking 100 restaurants to supply 10 names each.

2 Roisin wants to conduct an investigation to find out how much time Year 8 students spend watching TV.
   At her school there are five classes in Year 8, each of 30 students.
   a How should she obtain a stratified sample of 10% of Year 8?
      In each class, 40% are boys and 60% are girls.
   b How should this affect Roisin's sample?

3 In a large company there are four departments.
   These are the numbers of employees in each of the departments.

Department	Number of employees
A	175
B	50
C	250
D	125

   a Explain why the directors should take a stratified sample.
   b How many workers from each department should be selected for a sample of 60?
   c Describe how the directors should select their sample.

4 Comment on the method of sampling in each of these cases.
   a To find out how much support there is for a local football club, an interviewer stops the first ten people leaving a football match.
   b To find out how long cars stay in a pay-and-display car park, a researcher reads the time on the ticket of every tenth car in the car park.
   c A quality control technician takes samples from the production line at the beginning and end of each shift.

5 A researcher decides to take a sample of 200 people to find out what proportion of the population owns a car. Comment on these possible methods for choosing the sample.
   a Ask people returning to a car park in the evening.
   b Select names at random from the electoral register.
   c Ask people at random at a bus station one morning.

6 The table shows the number of employees working at two different locations in a large factory.

	Factory floor	Office
Number of staff	240	60

   The company director wants to take a stratified sample of 30 staff. Work out the number of employees he should survey from
   a the factory floor
   b the office.

7 The two way table shows the numbers of people who live in a small village.

	Adults	Children
Male	80	33
Female	110	27

A sample of 50 residents is to be questioned about the proposed development of a new recreational area in the village.
  a Given that the sample is stratified by gender, work out the numbers to be selected.
  b Given that the sample is stratified by age, work out the numbers to be selected.

8 A stratified sample was taken of the Year 8 pupils according to their method of travelling to school.
Eight in the sample travel by bus, five in the sample travel by car and three in the sample walk to school. Altogether 40 pupils travel by bus.

How many pupils in Year 8 **a** travel by car **b** walk **c** are there?

9 A stratified sample was taken of the men, women, boys and girls at a shopping centre. In the sample there were 9 men, 12 women, 3 boys and 6 girls.
At the shopping centre there were 80 women altogether.
  a How many men were there at the shopping centre altogether?
  b How many children were there at the shopping centre?

10 There were 128 builders, 40 engineers and 8 foremen at a large building site. A stratified sample was taken of the workers. 32 builders were in the sample.
  a How many foremen were in the sample?
  b How many engineers were in the sample?

11 At a conference, 75 physiotherapists, 200 doctors, 325 nurses and 100 radiographers attended. A stratified sample was taken of those attending the conference. 39 nurses were in the sample. How many people were in the sample altogether?

12 To monitor the number of birds of a particular species, 100 are trapped and tagged. The next month a sample of 60 birds of the same species are caught. 24 of them are found to be tagged. Calculate an estimate of the size of the population of this species of bird in the selected area.

13 To estimate the population of perch in a lake, 30 of the fish were caught, marked and released back into the lake. After 3 months a second sample of 20 perch was caught. Three of them were found to be marked. Calculate an estimate of the size of the population of perch in this lake.

14 A sample of 50 rabbits was taken from woodland in County Tyrone. Each rabbit was marked and released back into the woodland. A year later a sample of 30 rabbits was taken from the same area of woodland. Three of the rabbits in this sample were marked.
  a Calculate an estimate of the population of rabbits in this woodland area.
  b State one fault with the experiment and suggest how it could be improved.

CHAPTER 47

Probability

This chapter is about

- understanding and using relative frequency as an estimate of probability
- knowing and using the fact that the sum of all the probabilities is 1
- knowing that the probability of something happening is 1 minus the probability of it not happening
- knowing what is meant by mutually exclusive events
- knowing what is meant by independent events
- knowing what is meant by dependent events
- knowing and using the addition law of probability
- knowing and using the multiplication law of probability
- finding the probability of combined events
- using tree diagrams for independent events
- using tree diagrams for dependent events.

Exercise A

1   Pete rolls a dice 200 times and records the number of times each score appears.

Score	1	2	3	4	5	6
Frequency	29	34	35	32	34	36

   a   Work out the relative frequency of each of the scores correct to 2 decimal places.
   b   Do you think that Pete's dice is fair? Give a reason for your answer.

2   In a survey, 600 people were asked which flavour of crisps they preferred. The results are shown in the table.

Flavour	Frequency
Plain	166
Salt and vinegar	130
Cheese and onion	228
Other	76

   a   Work out the relative frequency for each flavour correct to 2 decimal places.
   b   Explain why it is reasonable to use these figures to estimate the probability of the flavour of crisps that the next person to be asked will prefer.

3   The owner of a petrol station notices that in one day 287 out of 340 people filling their car with petrol spent over £20.
   Use these figures to estimate the probability that the next customer will spend
   a   over £20   b   £20 or less.

4 Jasmine made a spinner numbered 1, 2, 3, 4 and 5.
She tested the spinner to see if it was fair. The results are shown below.

Score	1	2	3	4	5
Frequency	46	108	203	197	96

    a Work out the relative frequency of each of the scores correct to 2 decimal places.
    b Do you think that the spinner is fair?
       Give a reason for your answer.

5 The probability that Eric will have meat for lunch is 0.85.
What is the probability that he will not have meat for lunch?

6 The probability that I will have a drink of grapefruit juice with my breakfast is $\frac{5}{7}$.

What is the probability that I will not have a drink of grapefruit juice with my breakfast?

7 Nina, Christine and Jean are the only entrants for the Mathematics prize.
The probability that Nina wins is 0.3 and the probability that Christine wins is 0.45.
What is the probability that Jean wins?

8 Brian has a black, a green and a blue tie.
He decides to wear a tie.
The probability that he selects the black tie is 0.28 and the probability that he selects the green
tie is 0.51.
What is the probability that he selects the blue tie?

9 In an experiment, four mutually exclusive outcomes are possible: A, B, C and D.
P(A) = 0.12 P(B) = 0.34 P(C) = 0.27 Find P(D).

10 A biased five-sided spinner is numbered 1 to 5.
The table shows the probability of obtaining some of the scores when it is spun.

Score	1	2	3	4	5
Probability	0.37	0.1	0.14		0.22

    The spinner is spin once. Work out the probability of getting
    a 4   **b** 1 or 2   **c** 2 or 5   **d** an even number   **e** a prime number.

11 When Mrs Smith goes to town, the probability that she goes by bus is 0.5, in a taxi is 0.35 and
on foot is 0.15. Find the probability that she goes to town by
    a bus or taxi   **b** bus or on foot.

12 In any batch of televisions made by a company, the probabilities for the number of faults per
television are as follows.

Number of faults	0	1	2	3	4	more than 4
Probability	0.82	0.09	0.06	0.02	0.007	p

    a Find the value of p.
    b What is the probability that any particular television will have
       i one or two faults?   **ii** more than three faults?
       iii fewer than two faults?   **iv** at least one fault?

13 Katie has three black pens, five blue pens and two red pens in her bag.
She selects a pen at random. What is the probability that the pen is
    a red or blue?   **b** black or red?   **c** not red?

14 The probabilities of rolling each number on a biased dice are given in the table.

Number	1	2	3	4	5	6
Probability	0.1		0.09			0.27

Getting a 6 is three times as likely as getting a 4. Getting 5 is twice as likely as getting 2.

a Work out the probability of getting
    i 4   **ii** 5   **iii** 2

b The dice is rolled once. What is the probability of getting
    i 1 or 3? **ii** an odd number? **iii** a factor of 6? **iv** a prime factor of 10?

Exercise B

1 An ordinary dice is thrown and a coin is tossed.
What is the probability of getting a 6 and a tail?

2 The numbers on the menu show the probabilities that Richard chooses these dishes.

Menu		
First course	**Second course**	
Soup (0.6)	Spaghetti Bolognese	(0.1)
Melon (0.4)	Lamb Biryani	(0.7)
	Chicken & Mushroom Pie	(0.2)

What is the probability that Richard chooses soup and lamb biryani?

3 I take an ordinary dice and roll it twice.
What is the probability that I get an even number both times?

4 From experience, the probability of Sam winning a game of Solitaire is 0.7.
Sam plays two games.
a What is the probability that Sam wins the first game but loses the second?
b What is the probability that he loses both games?

5 On her way to work, Rami must go through a set of traffic lights and over a level crossing.
The probability that she has to stop at the traffic lights is 0.4. The probability that she has to stop at the level crossing is 0.3. These probabilities are independent.
a What is the probability that Rami does not have to stop at the traffic lights or the level crossing?
b Rami thinks that the probability she has to stop just once is 0.28.
Show why she is wrong.

6 On the way home I pass through three sets of traffic lights.
The probability that the first set is on green is 0.5.
The probability that the second set is on green is 0.6.
The probability that the third set is on green is 0.75.
Calculate the probability that
a I do not have to stop at any of the lights
b I have to stop at at least one set of traffic lights
c I have to stop at exactly two of the sets of lights.

7 A box contains seven red pens and three blue pens.
Jane takes a pen from the box and keeps it. Susan then takes a pen from the box.
Both girls take their pens without looking. Find the probability that Jane and Susan
   a both take red pens   **b** both take blue pens
   c take pens of the same colour   **d** take pens of different colours.

8 A bag contains two red counters, three white counters and four blue counters.
Three counters are drawn from the bag without replacement. Find the probability that
   a they are all red   **b** they are all blue
   c there is one of each colour   **d** there are at least two of the same colour.

9 A box contains four red, five blue and six green counters.
Two counters are selected at random, without replacement. Calculate the probability that
   a they are both the same colour   **b** exactly one of the counters is blue.

10 The letters of the word PREPOSSESSING are placed in a box.
A letter is selected and then replaced in the box and a second letter is then selected.
Find the probability that
   a the letter S is chosen twice   **b** the letter G is chosen twice   **c** a P and an E are chosen.

Exercise C

1 For breakfast, Lydia has either tea or coffee, and then either muesli, toast or grapefruit.
   a Draw a tree diagram to show all the possibilities.
   b Given that she is equally likely to choose any combination, find the probability that
      i she has coffee and grapefruit
      ii she does not have tea or grapefruit.

2 There are fifteen balls in a bag. Eleven of them are red and
the rest are white. Elias takes a ball at random, notes its
colour and replaces it. He then repeats the operation.
   a Copy and complete the tree diagram to show the choices.
   b Find the probability that Elias chooses
      i two white balls
      ii one of each colour.

First ball   Second ball

3 When Dani goes to work, she either goes in the car, cycles
or catches the bus. At lunchtime she either goes to the canteen, the gym or shopping. The
probability that she goes by car is 0.5 and the probability that she cycles is 0.2. The probability
that she goes to the canteen is 0.1 and the probability that she goes to the gym is 0.4.
   a Draw a tree diagram to show her possible choices
   b Find the probability that
      i she goes on the bus and goes shopping
      ii she cycles and goes to the gym or the canteen.

4 On his way to work, Mr Green always buys a newspaper and a drink. He buys the *Daily
Gazette* or the *Daily News* and for his drink he buys either mineral water or cola or orange.

The probability that he buys the *Daily Gazette* is $\frac{1}{3}$.

The probability that he buys a mineral water is $\frac{1}{5}$.

The probability that he buys a cola is $\frac{2}{5}$.

a Draw a tree diagram to show all the possibilities for the two purchases.

b Find the probability that

    i he buys the *Daily Gazette* and mineral water

    ii he buys the *Daily News* and not cola.

5 A class has 8 boys and 12 girls. Two students are selected at random from the class.

  a Draw a tree diagram to represent the two choices.

  b Calculate the probability that

    i they are both girls

    ii one is a boy and one is a girl.

6 A drawer contains six red socks and seven black socks. Two socks are taken from the drawer at random.

  a Draw a tree diagram to represent the two choices.

  b Calculate the probability that

    i both socks are black

    ii at least one sock is red.

7 The probability that it will rain on Saturday is 0.3.

If it rains on Saturday, then the probability that it will rain on Sunday is 0.5.

If it doesn't rain on Saturday, then the probability that it will rain on Sunday is 0.3.

  a Draw a tree diagram to show the probability of rain during the weekend.

  b Find the probability that it will rain on at least one day at the weekend.

8 The probability that the plum tree in my garden will produce more than 50 kg of plums in a given year is 0.6.

If the plum tree produces more than 50 kg of plums one year, then the probability that it will produce more than 50 kg of plums in the following year is 0.8; if it does not, then the probability is 0.4.

  a Draw a tree diagram to represent the probabilities of whether or not the plum tree will produce more than 50 kg of plums in two consecutive years.

  b Calculate the probability that the tree will

    i produce more than 50 kg of plums in both years

    ii produce more than 50 kg of plums in just one of the two years.

9 On his way to work, Owen has to drive through two sets of traffic lights.

The probability that the first set is green when he gets there is 0.6.

If the first set is green, then the probability that the second is also green when he gets there is 0.9, otherwise the probability is 0.2.

Find the probability that Owen will have to stop at just one set of lights.

10 It is estimated that 3 out of every 10 cars over 15 years old will fail the M.O.T. test because of a problem with their lights.

Of those that pass on lights, it is estimated that 4 out of 10 will then fail on brakes.

Of those that pass the test so far, 25% will then fail because of a problem with steering.

Find the probability that a car over 15 years old will pass these three checks of the M.O.T. test.

11 The probability that it will rain on a given day is 0.4.

If it rains one day, the probability that it will rain the next day is 0.7. If it does not rain that day, the probability that it will rain the next day is 0.2.

Find the probability that

  a it rains for three consecutive days

  b on three consecutive days it rains at least once.